Bridges

# Bridges

**Judith Dupré**

**Introductory interview with**
**Frank O. Gehry**

**Design by Alleycat**

Tess Press

# Contents

Published by
Black Dog & Leventhal Publishers, Inc.
151 West 19th Street
New York, NY  10011

Distributed by
Workman Publishing Company
708 Broadway
New York, NY  10003

Designed by Alleycat Design, Inc.

Manufactured in Hong Kong

Hardcover ISBN: 1-884822-75-4
h  g  f  e

Tess Press ISBN: 1-57912-417-8
h  g  f  e  d  c  b  a

Library of Congress Cataloging-in-Publication Data
Dupré, Judith
Bridges: a history of the world's most famous and important spans / Judith Dupré; design by Alleycat.
          p.          cm.
Includes bibliographical reference and index.
1. Bridges–History.   I. Alleycat Design (Firm)      II. Title.
TG15.D87 1997
624'.3–dc21

97-28291
CIP

Cover: Brooklyn Bridge by Jet Lowe for the Historic American Egineering Record, 1983.
Endpapers: The Rockville Bridge (1902) over the Susquehanna River in Harrisburg, Pennsylvania, is 3,830 feet (1,150 meters) in length and the longest stone arch bridge. Photograph by William Rau.
Page 1: Workers suspended from the cables of the Brooklyn Bridge, New York (1883).
Pages 2-3: Mackinac Bridge, St. Ignace-Mackinaw City, Michigan (1957).
Pages 4-5: The Tunkhannock Viaduct in Nicholson, Pennsylvania (1915), is the longest concrete railroad bridge in the world. Photograph by Richard Margolis. Map Illustrations by David Allen.

*For my mother and father*

# Foreword

Since the first log fell across water, people have been fascinated with bridges and their power to bring together what had been separate. Bridges can evoke exhilaration, triumph, and fear, sometimes simultaneously. They figure substantially in the myths, legends, and allegories of many cultures, with each century adding to the strata of symbolism. Consider the associative power of the monumental Brooklyn Bridge, the crossing at Chappaquidick, or a covered bridge across a quiet creek in Vermont.

Bridges span history. They have been built, burned, defended, crossed, and celebrated by kings, queens, monks, revolutionaries, and athletes, as well as by those of us who commute to work each day. Their story has been shaped by the elemental barrier of water and by the cities that grew up along the world's great waterways—imagine Paris, London, New York, or St. Petersburg without their signature bridges. Their many sizes and silhouettes reflect the unfolding of mankind's knowledge of technology and building materials, as well as the influence of military conquest, religious belief, and economics.

The earliest primitive bridges, formed from beams, stones, and ropes, evolved into more complex structures fashioned by highly intuitive, often anonymous hands. The Roman domination of the known world was in part attributable to their particular genius for engineering, manifested in their singular masonry arch bridges, many of which still stand today. Lesser known in the West are the exceedingly fine and innovative crossings constructed by the Chinese. Construction methods employed in the sixth-century Anji Bridge in Zhaoxian predate anything similar in the West by several hundred years. In the medieval world the construction of bridges fell to the religious orders and were funded by the faithful.

The Renaissance saw the rise of the inhabited bridge— exemplified by the Ponte Vecchio in Florence and the Rialto Bridge in Venice—and the Palladian bridge, which would not gain widespread currency until the eighteenth century, when Palladio's bridge designs were embraced by English landscape designers. The covered bridge, that most romantic of bridge types, is found throughout the world, but was particularly popular in a rapidly expanding young America, where wood was plentiful and time was at a premium.

The introduction of the steam locomotive in 1830 had a fundamental impact on bridge design, construction materials, and the nascent field of civil engineering. Stone and wood gave way to the use of iron, a material that was skillfully exploited by the giants of early-nineteenth-century rail bridge building in England, including Thomas Telford, Robert Stephenson, and Isambard Brunel. By century's end, the strength and lightness of a new material, steel, was manipulated with genius by James Eads, John Roebling, Benjamin Baker, and Gustave Eiffel.

Marcel Duchamp once said that America's only works of art were her plumbing and her bridges. Indeed, America's almost century-long monopoly on large-scale suspension bridge design began in 1883 with the completion of the Brooklyn Bridge and ended with the completion of the Verrazano Narrows Bridge in 1964. The next two decades saw a burst of large-scale bridge building in Europe, a

phenomenon that has been resurrected there and in Asia as the millennium approaches. Record-breaking bridges are now under construction in Japan, China, and Denmark. A variation of the suspension bridge, the cable-stayed bridge, was developed in the wake of World War II and has reached beyond utility to aesthetic expression in the contemporary works of Santiago Calatrava.

Engineers predict that a new type of bridge, a hybrid design incorporating suspension and cable-stayed features, will revolutionize long-span bridge design, as will high-strength, lightweight composite materials now being used in a handful of innovative bridges.

Bridges are vulnerable structures. Every day they withstand an assault of debilitating natural and man-made stresses. Although actual figures vary, a shockingly high percentage of bridges in the United States and other developed countries are in danger of collapse if repair is not forthcoming. Preventive measures, such as painting and seismic retrofitting, are costly, however, and do not

engender the same enthusiasm from taxpayers or legislators as new construction. At the same time, the growing awareness of the historic value of older bridges has led to their imaginative reuse as community landmarks, shops, and pizza parlors.

Bridge engineers, even those who have designed the largest, most costly, and best loved bridges, are not nearly as well known as the bridges they have built. A telling anecdote involves Robert Moses's introduction of Othmar Ammann, the builder of the Verrazano Narrows Bridge in New York, at the bridge's opening. After a string of well-deserved accolades, Moses inadvertently forgot to mention Ammann, the greatest bridge builder of the twentieth century, by name. The remarkable achievements of Ammann and other unsung heroes of the built environment are included within these pages.

Even before Leonardo da Vinci painted the enigmatic *Mona Lisa* with a semicircular arch bridge in the background, artists have been drawn to bridges as a subject. The bridge at Giverny was Monet's muse, the Pont Neuf

was Renoir's. Bridges peek from the corners or assume center stage in the paintings of Botticelli, Raphael, Constable, Whistler, Cézanne, van Gogh, to name a memorable handful. The Brooklyn Bridge, of course, is the most painted, sketched, photographed bridge in the world.

The bridges in the book are presented chronologically with the exception of the Ludendorff Bridge in Germany, which, though completed in 1918, is presented within the context of World War II, when it gained its place in history. The literary quotations and thematic spreads throughout the book illuminate the lyrical, catastrophic, utilitarian, and entertaining aspects of bridges, and the pull they have exerted on the collective and individual imagination.

The unassuming poetry of bridges reveals itself to those who would see them. Whether a simple crossing or an intricate labyrinth of steel, each of these structures has much to say about the extraordinary lives, effort, ingenuity, and wonder that come together on a bridge.

In the opinion of many, Frank O. Gehry is the most influential as well as the most original architect working today. By combining forms and materials in dramatic, unexpected ways, Gehry has created buildings that simultaneously distinguish and bridge the worlds of architecture, art, the media, and mass production. In 1989, he was awarded the Pritzker Architecture Prize, considered the highest honor in his profession.

*We propose. . . a bridge where sociality becomes the dominant practical purpose, a structure which allows for and suggests the unhurried appreciation of the complexities of views and activities on both sides of the river and on the river itself. We recognize that there is a potential to become something other than who we are through the constructs we build, and that these constructs can make us experience spaces and places anew.*

—Statement of Design Intent, Financial Times Millennium Bridge Competition, 1996

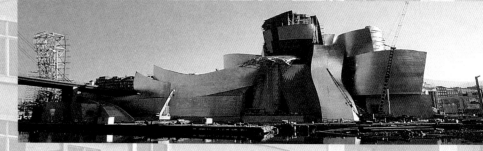

The new Guggenheim Museum (1997) sits on a far embankment of the Nervión River in the gritty port city of Bilbao, Spain. Clad in Spanish limestone and shimmering titanium "shingles," the vertical and horizontal volumes of Gehry's design have the appearance of a vast, free-form sculpture. Photo © Aitor Ortiz/Frank O. Gehry & Associates.

# Introductory Interview with Frank O

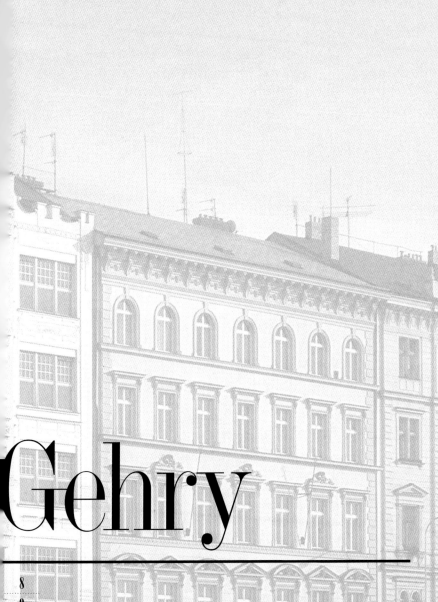

# Gehry

**Judith Dupré**
*Do you have a favorite bridge?*

**Frank O. Gehry**
I just saw a railroad bridge in Portugal I liked and photographed. A straight line with a single beam in the center. Simple. Beautiful. By Eiffel.

**JD**
*A favorite bridge city?*

**FOG**
I like London. I designed a footbridge across the Thames with Richard Serra, the artist, and Jörg Schlaich, an engineer with whom I had worked on other projects. He is the most brilliant structural engineer alive. [The *Financial Times* Millennium Bridge Competition] was a three-way collaboration, the most intense and integrated collaboration I have ever experienced. We spent hours into the night on conference calls discussing the project and faxing sketches.

The bridge was to join St. Paul's Cathedral—physically and visually—to the new Tate Gallery. The walk onto the landing was to be experienced as a proccasional, funnel-ing people from St. Paul's onto the bridge. The bridge's formal organization is layered with allusions to other bridges. Its arc recalled Japanese footbridges, while its trusses called up early railroad bridges. The arc culminated in a platform that can be read as a tabletop, deck, pier, dock, stage, balcony, etc. We hoped having the bridge end in a large-scale floating plaza [facing the Tate] would permit cultural and public events of all kinds.

**JD**
*Perhaps this collaboration—between architect, engineer, and artist—suggests a solution as to how aesthetics can be integrated into bridge design?*

**FOG**
Aesthetics are a quantifiable part of bridge design. It's the way an artist like Richard Serra and an architect like Frank Gehry could contribute to the visual part of the [Millennium Bridge], one that was being done by Jörg Schlaich, an engineer. [Schlaich] was open to it because he hadn't had that kind of collaboration before. When we lost he was very disappointed because he wanted to keep working with us. We just sent him a letter saying we wanted to resurrect the team for another project. He's ready to go. Why don't you talk to them?

*Structural engineer Jörg Schlaich is senior partner of Schlaich Bergermann und Partner in Stuttgart, Germany. For many years he was a consulting partner at the engineering firm of Fritz Leonhardt in Stuttgart. A professor at the University of Stuttgart, Schlaich has designed many footbridges and is particularly interested in the role of human scale in bridge design.*

**Jörg Schlaich**
The experience [of designing the Millennium Bridge] was positive for me in that each of us played a distinct role. Usually it is not easy for an architect and engineer to collaborate. The architect does the design, the engineer does the analysis. Frank and Richard did not try to design the bridge themselves. Instead they described what they envisioned and how users should feel about the bridge. They also explained that the bridge should be modest, flat, and fit into its surroundings, its urban context. Then, as the engineer, I had boundaries on which to base my proposals, which we in turn discussed and refined.

I have done many bridges, and usually hesitate to work with architects—although I have studied architecture myself—because they have their own design ideas and tend to reduce the engineer to determining materials and

Model of the *Financial Times* Millennium Bridge Competition entry by Frank Gehry, sculptor Richard Serra, and engineer Jörg Schlaich, 1996. Photo © Joshua White/Frank O. Gehry & Associates.

structure. This competition was different. The architect defined how the bridge should fit into the city; the artist, how it should touch its surroundings; and the engineer, how it could happen structurally. We were not competing but supplementing each other's roles, individual strengths that came together in the final design.

The [Millennium Bridge] was basically a truss. A truss is made up of struts and ties; ordinarily both components look the same. But in this case we differentiated them to illuminate the action of compression and tension: the struts were made from steel tubes, the ties from continuous cables. The bridge is cable-supported, although the cables are underneath the deck—Frank wanted a flat deck so nothing would obstruct the views of the city.

We must make people aware that a bridge in a city is as important as a museum. In former times, bridges really *were* part of a city. Take the Ponte Sant'Angelo and the Castel Sant'Angelo. They are a unit. Today we'd build the bridge and the castle separately—they would not be considered as a whole.

This sort of collaboration could raise the aesthetic levels of bridges being built today, which are, for the most part, substandard, with designs determined by economy, durability, and governing bodies. They are exchangeable and neutral. Each bridge is a new invention and should be defined within a subjective situation. With aesthetic input, an engineer can design a truly novel bridge.

*Richard Serra's large-scale abstract steel sculptures are in museum collections throughout the world. Snake, a specially commissioned 100-foot (30.5-meter)-long work by Serra, was the first piece to be installed in the new Guggenheim Museum in Bilbao, Spain.*

### Richard Serra

In my opinion, none of us alone would have ended up with this particular bridge. Instead, together, we made a bridge that is a hybrid. As a structure, it has many other readings—that it touched the other side of the river is secondary. What became apparent—because we were working on something that had a purpose— was that when someone came up with an expedient solution to a problem, the other two would recognize it immediately. For me the collaboration was fun, very inventive, and fruitful. I'd like to continue this dialogue.

The inherent minimalism of a bridge interests me. Frank and I have been talking about bridges for a while. We taught a course on bridges at Harvard during the eighties—using the bridge as a metaphor, a construct to engage a dialogue about connection, separation, spanning. Most of the students came up with monstrosities, but one kid spent the entire semester sanding a piece of balsa wood. In the end, his was the best, a simple curve.

Top: A freehand sketch by Frank Gehry of the Guggenheim Museum in Bilbao, Spain.

Above: A model of the Guggenheim Museum in Bilbao, Spain, shows the interaction of the museum's structure and the Puente de la Salve, a suspension bridge. Photo © Joshua White/Frank O. Gehry & Associates.

**JD**

*You have often said you work contextually. The Puente de la Salve, a steel suspension bridge, literally runs through the new Guggenheim Museum you designed in Bilbao, Spain. What opportunities did the site and the bridge present?*

**FOG**

Bilbao is a very contextual project, but not in a conventional manner. It is like a jujitsu move: trying to use the energies of the city to your advantage, to produce something new. A nineteenth-century industrial area on the waterfront is being redeveloped—the city's shipping industry has moved, they're bringing it closer to the sea—so it was chosen as the site for the museum. The site has a beautiful bend over the river, with the city above it. I liked the site because it was in the middle of the city and went under the bridge, and the fact that the bridge crossed into the heart of the city. . . . We were originally going to paint the bridge, but then I got attached to the site and started to like the bridge's color. It's dark green. Tom [Krens, director of the Guggenheim Foundation] is commissioning a piece for the bridge that will reach down to the museum.

**JD**

*Was the movement of the bridge a consideration?*

**FOG**

No, we kept the building away from it so its vibrations wouldn't affect the museum. The bridge slopes downward so the clearance beneath the bridge and above the museum ranges from 15 to 11 ½ feet [4.5 to 3.5 meters].

**JD**

*Many of your buildings incorporate water, while others are sited on rivers. What role does water play in your work?*

A footbridge leads to the main entrance of the Frederick R. Weisman Museum (1993). Located on the Mississippi River in Minneapolis, Minnesota, the art museum's luminous, multifaceted stainless steel facade reflects the water, as well as the changing light and seasons. Photo © Tim Griffith/Esto.

**FOG**

Well, I don't usually choose the sites, but, yes, the Minden-Ravensberg [Electric Company Offices, 1995] has a bridge that I put in to play with the reflective qualities of the building—a wooden bridge over a waterway. Wooden bridges feel good when you rub your hand over them. With the Schnabel Residence, I was sitting with Mr. [Rockwell] Schnabel on a lake in Finland having a vodka just as the sun was setting, and he said, "I'd like to take that home with me." So I gave that to him.

**JD**

*We experience bridges while moving across them. Your buildings also present ever-changing views as one moves around them. Could you address the idea of movement in your work?*

**FOG**

I was trained in a conventional architecture program and went through various apprenticeships by working with people who taught me how to detail marble and wood and metal and plaster and stone. I studied the details of Frank Lloyd Wright and the Greene brothers and Mies and Le Corbusier. Today you can't have the ornateness, the elegant detail, the carving of the last century—the budgets aren't there, the craftsmanship is not available. For me, movement is one way to create beauty and human scale, a twentieth-century form of ornament.

**JD**

*Your use of industrial materials such as chain link, corrugated aluminum, and plywood in your earlier buildings was considered radical.*

The Gehry House in Santa Monica, California (1978)—constructed of plywood, chain link, asphalt, and corrugated aluminum—proved a breakthrough project for the architect and effected a virtual revolution in the way architects think about forms and the materials used to construct them. Photo © Tim Street-Porter/Esto.

**FOG**

Yes . . . now I can use marble. Finally. [Laughter]

**JD**

*In your newer buildings you are working with the reflective qualities of metal exterior cladding.*

**FOG**

I am looking at light and luminosity and experimenting with different types of metals—stainless steel, zinc, and copper. In Bilbao we chose titanium for the facade because it glows in the rain—the city gets a lot of rain.

**JD**

*The new Guggenheim Museum has been hailed as the last architectural masterpiece of the twentieth century. What's next for you?*

**FOG**

We are doing the Coca-Cola Museum in Elizabethtown, Kentucky; the Samsung Museum of Modern Art in Seoul; Der Neue Zollhof—three office buildings—in Düsseldorf; and the Experience Museum, a new rock 'n' roll museum, in Seattle. This Sunday, though, I'm going sailing.

*Many thanks to Frank Gehry, Jörg Schlaich, Richard Serra, Joni Gottschalk, Keith Mendenhall, Holly Spiegel, Joshua White, Margot Zalbeygi, and Diane Alexander. —jd*

Pages 8–9: Nationale-Nederlanden Building, Prague, Czech Republic (1996). Photo © Tim Griffith/Esto. Pages 10–11: Guggenheim Museum in Bilbao, Spain. Photo © Aitor Ortiz/Frank O. Gehry & Associates..

This page, left to right:
A woman and her charge cross an appealing example of an ancient beam bridge in the Portuguese countryside near Tarouca Alcobaça.

The 102-foot span of the Pont St. Martin (25 B.C.), in a northern Italian town of the same name, is thought to be the longest of all Roman bridges.

The Pont de Langlois (c. 1820) is a drawbridge, or bascule, that opens over a canal in Arles, France. It is also called the Pont van Gogh because the artist painted it.

The Bridge of the Gods (1926) over Oregon's Columbia River clearly illustrates cantilever structure.

Every bridge, large or small, must withstand and overcome the forces or stresses to which it is subjected. Bridges are designed to carry their own weight, or *dead load*; to carry people and traffic, or *live load*; and to resist natural forces, such as wind and earthquakes, or *environmental load*.

The distance between the main supports of a bridge is its *span*, the length normally measured when describing the size of a bridge. A plank across a stream is a *simple span*. A *continuous span* is supported along its length by *piers*; the outermost supports are called *abutments*.

Four types of forces act on bridges, either singly or in combination: tension, compression, shear, and torsion. *Tension*, which stretches or pulls apart, is the opposite of *compression*, which squeezes or pushes together. *Shear* is a sliding force; *torsion* is a twisting force.

Bridges are based on one or more of three basic structures that are derived from forms found in nature: the *beam* from a log fallen across a stream, the *arch* from natural rock formations, and the *suspension* from a hanging vine. Though traditionally constructed from wood, stone, concrete, or steel, new bridges made from high-performance composite materials such as reinforced plastic are emerging.

The three types differ in the way each carries its own weight. The simplest, the beam bridge, is horizontally self-supporting and exerts a downward force on its piers. The *cantilever*, a more complex version of the beam bridge, is

# Basics

composed of two anchor arms that extend from opposite sides and are joined by a middle span, which is supported by piers. The arms support the midsection by the force of tension; the downward force is absorbed by the piers. Beam and cantilever bridges can be formed from a *truss*, a rigid structure usually built from triangular members. Truss spans can be simple or continuous, of the *deck type*, which is driven over, or the *through type*, which is driven through.

Arch bridges are characterized by their stability. In an arch, force is carried outward from the crown to the ends of the arch, where abutments exert a compressive force to keep the arch ends from spreading apart.

In the largest bridges, those of the suspension type, the main support members are parallel cables strung over towers that run the length of the bridge and are anchored at either end. The deck is supported by suspenders that are hung from the main cables. The weight of the bridge is supported by the cables, which are in tension, a pull withstood by their anchorages, and the towers, which are in compression. A variation is the *cable-stayed* bridge, in which the deck is attached directly to the towers by a series of diagonal cables.

Hybrid combinations of bridge types are extending their structural and aesthetic possibilities. Movable bridges, although variations on the basic trio, form a family of their own, described by the movement of the deck. To clear a navigation channel, a *swing bridge* deck pivots about a center point; a *bascule bridge* deck, or leaf, is raised with counterweights like a drawbridge; and a *lift bridge* deck is raised vertically, like a huge horizontal elevator.

This page, left to right:

Cable-stayed bridges, such as the angled Erasmus Bridge (1996) in Rotterdam, are constructed in an infinite variety of shapes.

Lights illuminate the main cables from which the deck of the Verrazano Narrows Bridge (1964) in New York is suspended.

The Trimmer Road Bridge in Spencerport, New York, is one of several nearly identical truss bridges spanning the Erie Canal.

A Strauss bascule bridge on the Cuyahoga River in Cleveland, Ohio, was abandoned and left in its open position.

Hybrid bridge structures include J. J. Arenas's and M. J. Pantaleon's arch-and-cable Puente de la Barqueta (1992) in Seville, Spain.

The Pont du Gard's top tier contains a cement-lined water channel that at one time was open to the public.

*I went through the three storeys of [the Pont du Gard] within which a feeling of respect almost prevented me from setting foot. The echo of my footsteps under these immense vaults made me imagine that I heard the sturdy voices of those who had built them. I felt myself lost like an insect in this immensity. I felt, in spite of my sense of littleness, as if my soul was somehow or other elevated, and I said to myself with a sigh, "Why was I not born a Roman?"*

—Jean Jacques Rousseau, The Confessions, 1781–88

**PONT DU GARD**

Uzès
River Gard
Nîmes
Rhône
France
Mediterranean

# Pont du Gard

Remains of sixteen Roman aqueducts are found in Spain. Pictured here is the aqueduct at Segovia, consisting of two tiers of 199 spans constructed of granite laid without mortar, that extends 2,624 feet (800 meters). Built in A.D. 41–54, it is still in use.

Although the Romans were not the first to build bridges, they were first to build large-scale bridges, many of which have survived two millennia of wars, floods, and human intervention. Some of the greatest Roman bridges were aqueducts, designed to carry not people but water, which was nearly as important to the Romans as military conquest.

The largest and arguably one of the most beautiful Roman aqueducts is the Pont du Gard, completed in 18 B.C. It crosses the Gard River in southern France, and is part of an aqueduct system that once carried water a distance of 31 miles (50 kilometers) to the ancient city of Nemausus, now Nîmes. The Pont du Gard's sheer size, coupled with its harmonious design and excellent state of preservation, make it a milestone in the legendary history of Roman engineering.

Given their facility with the voussoir arch, an art they appropriated from the earlier Greeks and Etruscans, the Romans could span almost any river. The superbly proportioned Pont du Gard stands approximately 155 feet (47 meters) tall (the highest Roman bridge and an exception to the typical Roman waterwork, which channeled water at ground level or through underground pipes). It consists of two tiers of semicircular arches formed from stones, each cut to fit perfectly against its neighbor; only the top tier is cemented. These wedge-shaped stones, known as voussoirs, when arranged in an arch, exerted a downward as well as an outward thrust. The bridge's piers are only a fifth as thick as the arch spans are long, instead of the customary 1:3 ratio of most Roman bridges, giving the structure a graceful, slender silhouette surpassed only by the aqueduct at Segovia, which has a 1:8 ratio of pier thickness to span length.

It is generally believed that the Pont du Gard was constructed under the direction of Marcus Vipsanius Agrippa (64–12 B.C.), the son-in-law of Emperor Augustus and his highest official. Agrippa had the tenacity and technical competence to see through to completion major construction projects, first in Rome and then in Nîmes, where most of the Roman ruins outside of Rome are located. In his comprehensive book *Roman Bridges*, Colin O'Connor describes the complex hierarchy of Roman officials, architects, mathematicians, engineers, surveyors, militia, and laborers whose efforts were precisely orchestrated in the Romans' unprecedented building program, which left its distinctive stamp on every corner of the then known universe.

A misguided attempt to widen the pedestrian passage in the seventeenth century almost caused the Pont du Gard's collapse. It was restored, first in 1669 and again in 1855. Today, protected as a UNESCO World Heritage site, the Pont du Gard is an eloquent witness to the strength of the voussoir arch and the enduring engineering legacy of the Romans.

The two lower tiers are composed of broad arches; the longest one, which crosses the river, is 80 feet (24 meters) wide. The protruding stones supported scaffolding during construction.

| Crossing | Gard River | Designer/Engineer | Marcus Vipsanius Agrippa | Completed | 18 B.C. | Length | 886 feet/270 meters | Materials | masonry | Type | aqueduct |
|---|---|---|---|---|---|---|---|---|---|---|---|

*A cofferdam, with its sides formed of oaken stakes with ties between them, is to be driven down into the water and firmly propped there; then, the lower surface inside, under the water, must be leveled off and dredged…and finally, concrete… must be heaped until the empty space which was within the cofferdam is filled up.*

—Vitruvius, De Architectura, c. 27 B.C.

Ponte Sant'Angelo, Rome

Hadrian (reigned A.D. 114-38), the brilliant, moody emperor of Rome during the height of its material prosperity, traveled with a contingent of "geometers, architects, and every sort of expert in construction and decoration," according to an ancient source. The Ponte Sant'Angelo leads to his mausoleum, a great circular structure later renamed Castel Sant'Angelo.

# Ponte Sant'Angelo

By the second century B.C., the Romans had mastered two crucial aspects of bridge building that ensured the stability and longevity of their spans: the construction of a midstream foundation and the arch it supported. Six of the eight stone bridges they built over the Tiber between 200 B.C. and A.D. 260 still stand. The most celebrated of these, Hadrian's Aelius Bridge, now called the Ponte Sant'Angelo, is a good example of the Roman construction methods that made crossing deep water possible.

The Ponte Sant'Angelo consists of stone-arch spans, the longest of which is 60 feet (18 meters). The 24-foot (7 meter)-high piers, the only part of the original bridge that remains, rest on foundations that are built 16 feet (5 meters) below the riverbed. To build foundations in the Tiber, a wide river with a mud bed, the Romans made use of a temporary enclosure called a cofferdam. As described in the engineer Vitruvius's seminal treatise, *De architectura (On Architecture,* c. 27 B.C.), a cofferdam

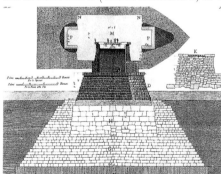

was made from a ring of wooden piles driven into the riverbed to form a sheath.

**A drawing by Piranesi of the bridge's central pier shows its immense substructure. At the top of the plan is a view of the pier's elongated cutwater.**

Once the water was pumped out, exposing the bottom for construction, the cofferdam was filled with a waterproof concrete called *pozzolana,* made from lime, sand, water, and ground volcanic rock found near the city of Pozzuoli; its discovery by the Romans critically advanced their ability to build pier foundations.

The use of the stone arch allowed long spans to be built that were more permanent than wood. The use of a self-supporting semicircular arch, as opposed to a shallow arch, which requires strong side-bracing, made it possible, in the words of bridge historian David J. Brown, "for the Roman engineers to build their bridges out from the shore a span at a time—cofferdam, then foundations, then pier, then arch—rather than having to go through the much more difficult operation of putting the entire bridge substructure in position first."

Though excellent engineers, the Romans were not perfect. Having claimed the semicircular arch as their own, they showed little interest in exploring other structures that might have saved them considerable time and expense. Their foundations—in some instances not deep enough, in others not strong enough—plagued them and required that many bridges be rebuilt. When the Romans succeeded, however, as with the Ponte Sant'Angelo, their bridges seem nearly eternal.

**Ten graceful statues of angels, after designs by Baroque master Gian Lorenzo Bernini, were mounted on the parapets in 1688.**

| **Crossing** Tiber River | **Designer/Engineer** Hadrian | **Completed** A.D. **134** | **Span** 60 feet/18 meters | **Materials** masonry | **Type** arch |

*The Anji Bridge, admired and treasured through the centuries, still stands as a monument to early Chinese achievements in both engineering and aesthetic expression.*
—Ronald G. Knapp, "Bridge on the River Xiao," Archaeology, 1988

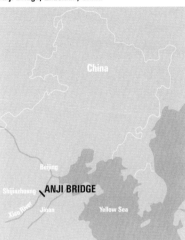

Anji Bridge, Zhaoxian, China

# Anji Bridge

**E**ight hours southwest of Beijing, where the Xiao River flows over the North China Plain, stands the remarkable Anji Bridge. Designed by Li Chun in the late sixth century, the Anji marks the first time a segmental stone arch design was used in bridge construction. Predating anything comparable in Europe by eight hundred years, it also pioneered open spandrel construction, which lightened the bridge's mass, an innovation not seen in the West until the nineteenth century.

Also called the Zhaozhou or Great Stone Bridge, the Anji was built during the powerful though short-lived Sui Dynasty (A.D. 581–617). During the Sui period, a number of monumental engineering feats were initiated, including the Grand Canal and the reconstruction of the Great Wall, as well as a host of smaller projects aimed at facilitating the movement of the military and commercial goods.

In his authoritative book *Chinese Bridges*, one of the few works on this subject available in English, Ronald G. Knapp describes the conditions that determined the design and construction of the Anji. The wide, swiftly moving Xiao River prohibited the use of multiple stone piers. A single semicircular arch, which would have reached a height of 66 feet (20 meters), was also ruled out. A flat beam bridge would have accommodated the steady stream of pedestrians, animals, and carts crossing the river but would not have provided enough clearance for boats. Li

A grimacing, open-mouthed *taotie*, the mythical beast depicted on the bridge's central balustrade, was placed there to protect it from floods.

Chun solved this conundrum by designing a longer, flatter arch that used a fraction, or segment, of a circle rather than a full semicircle to achieve both sufficient height and a gentle incline. To reduce the weight and pressure exerted by the arch, the spandrels—the triangular areas between the arch and the roadway— were pierced.

Twenty-eight parallel arches, formed from massive wedges of limestone reinforced with iron, give the bridge great flexibility. The stones, quarried nineteen miles away, were moved to the construction site only in winter, when they could be dragged over ice; the bridge took at least a decade to complete.

According to an eighth-century Tang chronicle, the uncluttered silhouette of the bridge was originally complemented by ornamental bas-relief carvings of interlocked dragons and beasts. They had disappeared by the time the bridge was first studied in 1934, but some were discovered in a later excavation and are now displayed nearby.

The Anji Bridge, still in use after 1,400 years, ushered in a new era of bridge building in China. In the centuries that followed, many similar spans would be built, although none would earn the accolades accorded the elegant Anji by a Ming Dynasty poet who compared it to a "new moon rising above the clouds, a long rainbow drinking from a mountain stream."

The superb craftsmanship of the bridge is evident in a detail of an open spandrel that shows the iron and stone work used to stabilize the voussoirs.

| | | | | | |
|---|---|---|---|---|---|
| Crossing **Xiao River** | Designer/Engineer **Li Chun** | Completed **late 6th century** | Length **131 feet/40 meters** | Materials **limestone** | Type **arch** |

*In the Middle Ages the hope of a spiritual reward in the afterlife was a powerful motivating force behind gifts to endow churches, to build bridges, and to relieve the indigent and ill.*

—Marjorie Nice Boyer, Medieval French Bridges, 1976

Throughout the Middle Ages, monks administered the construction of bridges, which were considered pious works. Contributions and bequests to bridges were encouraged by the clergy, who rewarded donors with indulgences, or pardons of sin.

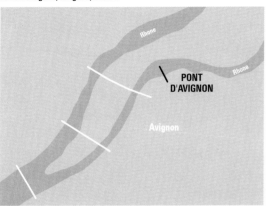

# Pont d'Avignon

ocal legend has it that in 1178 a total eclipse of the sun occurred at Avignon. The frightened towns-people gathered in the marketplace, where they were addressed by the bishop. He was interrupted by a ragged shepherd, Bénezet, who said the eclipse was a sign from God that he should build a bridge. In response to the bishop's demand for proof, Bénezet lifted a massive stone and carried it to the place where the bridge was to be built. The people, recognizing the hand of God, commissioned Bénezet to build the bridge. On the basis of this miracle, recognized by the Catholic Church, Bénezet was canonized. The bridge is also known as the Pont Saint Bénezet. Another version of the bridge's genesis is provided by Viollet-le-Duc, the nineteenth-century architectural historian, who credited its design to a group of monks who built it under the direction of Brother Benoît.

Whichever story is true, the fact remains that the rapidly expanding medieval infrastructure demanded new bridges. This work was overseen by monks who were enjoined to "build bridges and streets and thus prepare your way to heaven." Their charitable duties included the protection of travelers, both merchants and pilgrims, of which there were thousands. Hospitals and shelters built by such brotherhoods proliferated, especially at river crossings. Their construction, along with that of bridges, was financed by the donations of the faithful, who were promised a spiritual reward in the afterlife.

The original specifications of the Pont d'Avignon are unknown, though it is believed to have been nearly 3,000 feet (900 meters) long. The bridge crossed the river where it is split by the island of Barthelasse; to reduce the effects of flooding, the bridge's western branch, now destroyed, was bent at a 30-degree angle. It was composed of a series of 20 or 21 graceful, elliptical arches, each with a span greater than 100 feet (30.5 meters) and rising on piers 25 feet (7.6 meters) thick. To protect the town from invaders, the bridge was built with an extremely narrow roadway—a mere 6½ feet (2 meters) wide on the Avignon side—that could be defended easily.

In 1226 the city was seized by Louis VIII, who ordered the bridge destroyed. The Avignonais repaired the bridge, though less skillfully this time. The structure became more vulnerable and—with the exception of the four arches that still stand today —was destroyed by a series of floods during the seventeenth century.

*Sur le pont d'Avignon,*
*L'on y danse, l'on y danse;*
*Sur le pont d'Avignon,*
*L'on y danse, tout en rond.*
—Traditional French folk song

Bridges, frequently employed by the Church as a metaphor for the dangers inherent in the soul's passage, were often decorated with effigies of saints. Many bridges had chapels, some more than one. For five hundred years Bénezet was buried at the chapel on his bridge; his body now rests at Saint-Didier in Avignon.

| Crossing | Rhône River | Designer/Engineer | unknown | Completed | 1187 | Original length | 3000 feet/900 meters | Materials | masonry | Type | arch |

*Ponte Vecchio, combining as it did a piazza for mingling, a bustling marketplace, and, at one end, a hospital . . . could be regarded as a concentrated version of the city itself.*
—R.W.B. Lewis, The City of Florence, 1995

Centuries of additions and annexes give the bridge its distinctive, irregular configuration.

**Ponte Vecchio, Florence, Italy**

Florence

Carraia
Arno
S. Trinita
Duomo

PONTE VECCHIO

River
Palazzo Vecchio

Grazie

Palazzo Pitti

# Ponte Vecchio

T he Ponte Vecchio is more than a bridge. It is a street, a marketplace, a public square, and an enduring icon of Florence, a city whose identity has long been defined by its bridges and the turbulent river they cross.

The first substantial bridge across the Arno, built after the flood of 1177, was covered with shops and residences, an inhabited bridge peculiar to and common throughout Europe in the Middle Ages. Butchers, tanners, and farmers hawked their goods from the shops lining its roadway, the rental of which financed new public works. Three more bridges, the Santa Trinità, Nuovo (now Carraia), and Rubaconte (now Grazie), were built to handle the city's expansion; by 1218 the oldest bridge began to be referred to as the Vecchio (old) in order to distinguish it from the newer ones.

The Ponte Vecchio, connecting the two halves of the walled city of Florence, was at the same time its social and commercial hub. It withstood periodic assaults by fire and water until it succumbed to an apocalyptic flood in 1333, devastating the city's inhabitants. Though debated, the present design is generally attributed to Taddeo Gaddi (c. 1300–1366), better known as a painter and disciple of Giotto.

In a radical departure, Gaddi did not use the semicircular arch favored by the Romans but a shallow segmental arch that, though unknown in Europe at the time, had been used in China centuries earlier (see page 19). Because it required fewer piers than a semicircular arch, a segmental arch facilitated navigation; the low pitch of its roadway made it easier for animal-drawn carts to cross.

The massive piers are finished with pointed cutwaters to reduce their resistance to the current. In the center Gaddi left a piazza—described by fifteenth-century architectural theorist Leon Battista Alberti as the chief ornament of the city—for citizens to gather, debate, and enjoy the river view.

In 1565 Duke Cosimo I de' Medici decided to remodel. His plans, put into effect by the great architect Giorgio Vasari, included the construction of a roofed passageway that would stretch from the Uffizi over the Ponte Vecchio and arrive ultimately at the Pitti Palace. The route, entirely and symbolically above street level, would be used by the duke and his court. Not surprisingly, a decree ordering the removal of the bridge's more odoriferous tenants was soon effected; henceforth the bridge would become the obligatory abode of the city's goldsmiths and money changers. Luxury goods have been sold there since.

The Arno again surged over its banks in 1966, nearly obliterating the city. Florentines who experienced the disastrous flood said it was almost worse than the events of August 3, 1944. On that night German bombers reduced to rubble all of Florence's bridges, with the exception of the Ponte Vecchio, which was spared by direct order of Hitler.

After the war, imaginative plans were put forth to rebuild the area surrounding the Ponte Vecchio, but in the end it was decided that things should remain as they had always been. At the heart of the picturesque jumble of banks, restaurants, and hotels that quickly sprang up to replace those that had been destroyed is the Ponte Vecchio.

**Crossing** Arno River   **Designer/Engineer** Taddeo Gaddi   **Completed** 1345   **Length** 330 feet/100 meters   **Materials** masonry   **Type** arch

On November 9, 1993, after almost twenty-four hours of artillery fire, the Old Bridge collapsed and sank into the river. It has been replaced by a metal suspension bridge.

# Mostar Bridge

*...they had always been concerning themselves with the bridge; they had cleaned it, embellished it, repaired it down to its foundations, taken the water supply across it, lit it with electricity and then one day blown it all into the skies as if it had been some stone in a mountain quarry and not a thing of beauty and value, a bequest.*

—Ivo Andric, The Bridge on the Drina, 1959

Following the disastrous losses of art and architectural treasures in Europe during World War II, the Convention for the Protection of Cultural Property in the Event of Armed Conflict was signed at The Hague in 1954. The treaty states that cultural heritage is a basic human right worthy of international respect and protection. The treaty, sadly, did not save Mostar, the four-hundred-year-old bridge that had given the city of Mostar its life, name, and prominence as an intercontinental crossroads between the East and the West.

Mostar, a major town in Bosnia and Herzegovina, straddled both banks of the Neretva River. It was named for the bridge at its heart, the Stari Most, or "Old Bridge," as the structure was commonly called. A masterpiece of Ottoman engineering, the single-arch stone bridge was designed in the sixteenth century by the Turkish engineer Hajrudin for the emperor Suleyman the Magnificent.

The city that grew up around the bridge became a commercial and cultural center favored by Muslims, Croats, and Serbs alike. Despite conflicts in the region throughout its history, Mostar's mosques, synagogues, and churches—all located within close proximity to one another—stood for centuries as a visible sign of the intermingled lives of its various communities.

Mostar saw some of the heaviest fighting in the Bosnian conflict. The brutal war of 1993 between the Serbs and Muslims literally ripped the city in two: the Old Bridge was destroyed. In the name of "ethnic cleansing," hundreds of irreplaceable architectural treasures in the Balkans were torched, dynamited, and bulldozed—an attempt, it seems, to eradicate a culture by destroying the very places where the people had gathered to live their lives.

In happier times, children would thrill tourists by jumping from the bridge into the water below for a few coins.

Slowly, the city of Mostar is being rebuilt. While the loss of human life is the paramount tragedy of the Bosnian wars, the survival of architecture and the cultural memory it embodies, once symbolized by a bridge in Mostar, is important to the survival of people as well.

Centuries of commerce over the bridge had polished its limestone treads smooth.

| Crossing | Neretva River | Designer/Engineer: | Hajrudin | Completed | 1566 | Length | 90 feet/27 meters | Materials | stone | Type | arch |
|---|---|---|---|---|---|---|---|---|---|---|---|
| | | | | Destroyed | 1993 | | | | | | |

*The mere use of one's eyes in Venice is happiness enough.*
—Henry James, Italian Hours, 1909

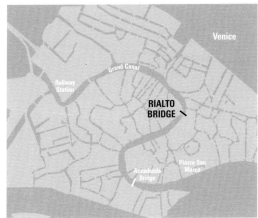

Venice's Bridge of Sighs, so called because wailing prisoners were taken over it into the adjacent prison, was designed by da Ponte's nephew Antonio Contino.

# Rialto Bridge

*I think one of the great moments of the Grand Canal occurs when you swing around the bend beside the fish market and see the Rialto there before you, precisely as you have imagined it all your life, one of the household images of the world, and one of the few Venetian monuments to possess the quality of geniality.*

—James Morris, The World of Venice, 1960

Venice, that most improbable and fantastic of cities, is cobbled together with bridges of every size and description and has more bridges per square mile than anywhere else. Here one finds bridges with names such as the Bridge of Fists, Bridge of Straw, Bridge of the Honest Woman, Bridge of Courtesy, Bridge of Humility, Bridge of Paradise, Bridge of Sighs, as well as the Little Bridge, the Long Bridge, and the city's best known bridge, the Rialto Bridge.

At the narrowest stretch of the Grand Canal is the Rialto, the commercial heart of the city, where both residents and tourists mingle. The bridge there—always called by the Venetians the Ponte di Rialto, to distinguish it from the district—is one of many that have crossed the site over the centuries. The earliest was a pontoon bridge built in 1173. The next, constructed of wood, was destroyed during the Tiepolo revolution in 1310. The weight of the crowd thronging to see the marriage of the Marquis of Ferrara in 1444 made short work of the next. It was replaced by a grand wooden bridge with shops and a central draw-bridge that stood until the middle of the sixteenth century, when the decision was made to rebuild it in stone.

In what was possibly the most distinguished architectural competition ever held, the city elicited proposals from the pantheon of Renaissance artists, including Michelangelo, Sansovino, and Palladio. Palladio's proposal for a five-arched, colonnaded bridge was published in his *Quattro Libri dell' Architettura* (*Four Books of Architecture*, 1570) and inspired a host of imitators (see pages 32–33). In the end, the commission went to the appropriately named, lesser known architect Antonio da Ponte, who, with his nephew Antonio Contino, built the single-arch marble bridge between 1588 and 1591. Two rows of shops and a center roadway are concealed within its arcades.

The bridge has survived floods, earthquakes, and ridicule; it is mocked to this day by the classically minded for being lumpy, awkward, a white elephant. Many painters, however, fondly depicted it, including Canaletto (1697–1768), whose minutely detailed view of the bustling Rialto appears here. Loved or not, the Rialto Bridge has become a symbol of Venice, an icon so enduring that its actual appearance has little influence on the passion people feel for it.

The bridge at Wilton House, England (1737), was the first of many to be modeled after Palladio's proposed bridge over the Rialto.

The bridge includes a depiction of the Annunciation: on the left-hand side of the arch is the angel Gabriel; on the other, the Virgin receives news of the imminent birth of Christ. John Ruskin, in his epic *The Stones of Venice* (1853), singles out the portrayal of Mary as the bridge's loveliest detail because of the way she lies on a flat plane, anchored firmly in the terrestrial. The center banner obscures a dove representing the Holy Spirit.

| Crossing | Grand Canal | Designer/Engineer | Antonio da Ponte | Completed | 1591 | Span | 89 feet/27 meters | Materials | marble | Type | arch |

*Not a single thing
Have I closely observed;
My feet on life's way
Are too vigorous.*
—Mori Ogai (1862–1922)

While most vehicular bridges tend to go unnoticed, made invisible by routine commuting, foot bridges found in gardens and parks are not only noticed but celebrated. In a garden there is pause. In a garden the science and art of the bridge, its role in defining the edge between mankind and nature, can be contemplated.

Although aware that they are biologically and physiologically part of nature, people through the ages have been driven to dominate and conquer nature with technological works, such as bridges, that prove mankind's mastery over nature. The history of garden design reflects one or the other of these two conflicting attitudes. The Japanese garden is inspired by the idea that humanity is a part of nature; Renaissance gardens, by the idea that humans are nature's masters. As transitional points between what is natural and what is manmade, garden bridges are charged with symbolism and meaning.

The first traditional Japanese gardens emerged during the Heian period (784–1185) and were influenced by earlier Chinese gardens, whose refined design was shaped by Taoist and Buddhist values of harmony, order, and balance. To induce contemplation, gardens were carefully calculated as a series of linked but distinct sensations. By framing views and controlling the experience of the garden, bridges were and remain an important element of the highly codified spatial and symbolic compositions of Oriental gardens. Touching both sides, but belonging to neither, bridges express the many dichotomies of life: order and spontaneity, depth and surface, permanence and change, stillness and movement. Appropriately, *hashi* is the word for both "bridge" and "edge" in Japanese.

The placement of stepping-stone bridges like this one at the Heian Jingu shrine in Kyoto, Japan, appears both random and fortuitous.

The formal geometric gardens of seventeenth-century France, epitomized by André le Nôtre's gardens at Versailles for Louis XIV, became, in the hands of the English, romantic paeans to nature's thrilling wildness. With the eighteenth-century movement back to nature, Palladian bridges, along with other classical architectural follies, were inserted into the vistas of great English private estates as conspicuous ornaments (see page 33).

Frederick Law Olmsted (1822–1903) and Calvert Vaux (1824–1895) continued this romantic pastoral tradition when they were commissioned to design New York's Central Park in 1858. In the matter of the park's bridges, however, they broke from the English tradition. Convinced that nature, without artifacts, was the only antidote to the park's fiercely urban setting, they concealed the bridges—some forty in all, no two alike—with skillful grading so they would not be seen until the stroller was upon them.

Exuberantly painted ceramics adorn the bridge at the Plaza de España in Seville, Spain. It was designed by Hannibal Gonzalez for the 1929 Ibero-American Exposition.

The Bow Bridge (1862), the best known bridge in Central Park, is the oldest extant wrought-iron girder bridge in America.

# Garden Bridges

The representation of bridges also exerted a strong pull on Japanese fine artists, most notably Katsushika Hokusai (1760–1849) and Ando Hiroshige (1797–1858), who integrated bridges into the landscapes of many of their woodblock prints. Exported abroad in the nineteenth century, the content and compositions of their work had a marked influence on the Impressionists. The most memorable Impressionist paintings of bridges were by Claude Monet (1840–1926), who by the end of 1890 was making enough from the sales of his work to buy property at Giverny. His improvements to the garden there included damming a stream to form a pond over which he built a bridge "in Japanese taste" that he immortalized in his lush and atmospheric Japanese Bridge series.

Bridge, landscape, and weather are perfectly integrated in this work by Japanese master printer Hiroshige.

The wooden bridge at Giverny, surrounded by waterlilies, irises, and wisteria, figured prominently in Monet's later paintings.

*Although practically rebuilt a few years ago, [the Pont Neuf] is still standing and in use—*
*with a life story of over three hundred years.*
—David B. Steinman and Sara Ruth Watson, *Bridges and Their Builders*, 1941

# Pont Neuf

D espite its name, the Pont Neuf (New Bridge) is the oldest and most celebrated of the thirty-two bridges in Paris. Since its completion in 1609, the Pont Neuf has been to Paris what the heart is to the human body, "the center of all movement," as author Louis Sébastien Mercier put it in the 1780s. Construction of the bridge began in 1578 under the direction of Henry III (1551–1589) and was completed during the reign of the enormously popular Henry IV (1553–1610), who still presides over the bridge, reincarnated as a bronze equestrian statue that faces the triangular Place Dauphine, one of the city's first royal squares.

In the early seventeenth century, under the able reign of Henry IV, Paris emerged from the devastation of a half century of war to become the political and social fulcrum of Europe. The Pont Neuf was but one element of Henry IV's passionate orchestration, with the assistance of his brilliant minister the duc de Sully, of the restoration of his beloved city. During the twenty-one years of his reign until his assassination in 1610, he transformed a ravaged medieval Paris into a model of civic design.

The Pont Neuf was built to connect the two halves of Paris with its original core, the Île de la Cité. Supported in the middle by the tip of the island, the masonry bridge extends in five arches from the Left Bank and in seven from the Right. As designed by Baptiste Androuet Du Cerceau (1560?– 1602?) with Pierre des Illes, who may have made use of an earlier design by Guillaume Marchand, the bridge is an asymmetrical combination of semicircular arches, no two alike. The spans, which range from 31 to 61 feet (9 to 19 meters), not only vary in comparison to one another but differ on the upstream and downstream sides of the same arch. The bridge's foundations were completely rebuilt under Napoleon III, together with the arches of the long arm, which were made elliptical.

At each pier, the parapet curves out toward the water to form half-moon bays, which were filled with a dizzying array of vendors until they were banished in 1756. John Russell makes a witty inventory of them in his book *Paris*, describing the Pont Neuf as a place where "you could have a tooth pulled out, go through the 'Help Wanted,' watch the tightrope dancers, buy a Lancret or a Fragonard, join the army, pick up the new book by Marivaux or a first edition of *Manon Lescaut*, arrange to go up in a balloon, watch a bullfight, take fencing lessons, and attend a surgical demonstration."

The immortal Pont Neuf remains the busy center of Parisian life.

In September 1985, under the direction of artists Christo and Jeanne-Claude, three hundred workers transformed the bridge by wrapping it completely in silky golden fabric and rope for a period of fourteen days. "The Pont Neuf Wrapped" emphasized the proportions of the bridge, while recalling the extravagant changes and additions it has undergone over the years. The expenses were paid by the artists.

Henry IV ruled with ebullient flair yet absolute authority. He endeared himself to the French peasantry with the homely promise of "a chicken in his pot every Sunday." It was said that before the Pont Neuf was completed, he jumped from pier to pier until he had traversed its length.

| Crossing Seine River | Designer/Engineer Baptiste Androuet Du Cerceau | Completed 1609 | Length 761 feet/232 meters | Materials masonry | Type arch |

*For the architects of the English landscape garden, the quotation of the Palladian bridge, even in a free ensemble, signified both an homage and an obligation.*
— Jan Pieper, "Palladian Bridges," Daidalos, 1995

In the eighteenth century wooden truss bridges were often called Palladian bridges. This one, the much admired Mathematical Bridge at Queens' College in Cambridge, England, was pegged, not nailed, together in 1749.

Palladian Bridge, Buckinghamshire, England

# Palladian Bridge

Andrea Palladio (1508–1580), the most influential architect of the Italian Renaissance, was the first to publish extensively on the subject of bridges. In the third book of his *Quattro Libri dell' Architettura* (1570), Palladio reconstructed various antique Roman bridges and published plans and elevations for wood and masonry bridges, including the design for the Rialto Bridge (see page 27). Through his writing and buildings, Palladio's ideas were exported from Venice to such far-flung places as the United States, Imperial Russia, and the West Indies, as well as throughout Europe, and were embraced for their fundamental clarity and harmonious proportions.

In the early eighteenth century Palladio was domesticated in rural England. British gardeners, tired of the formal geometry of French gardens, began to create luxuriant gardens for their wealthy patrons that, although in truth highly orchestrated, appeared to be Nature at her most natural. In the new English garden, the landscape had a relaxed, irregular form featuring expanses of grass, groves of trees, and artful artificial lakes.

Beginning in 1730 under the direction of William Kent (1685–1748) and later Lancelot "Capability" Brown (1716–1783), the grounds at Stowe House, a vast estate in Buckinghamshire, England, were transformed into the new style of garden. The Stowe landscape, which would evolve over a century, also contains some thirty-eight architectural ornaments, or follies, including a bridge derived from Palladio's design, which impart an antique and classical character to the estate. There is no known record of who—Kent, Brown, or another party—designed the Palladian Bridge.

The Palladian Bridge, as well as its near twin at Wilton House (see page 27), is less a copy of the Rialto plan than a reassemblage of Palladio's characteristic elements. Like the Rialto Bridge, it includes an Ionic colonnade, arched and pedimented end pavilions, and stepped approaches. The bridge—one of many follies encountered by strollers meandering along the estate's paths—is placed between the formal gardens and the grounds landscaped in the new English style.

Throughout the ages and across cultures, bridges have been used as symbols of transition. They have been employed as potent metaphors for the soul's dangerous passage to the afterworld and, in more contemporary times, as symbols of the passage of time and the stages of life's journey. Within the English garden, as discussed in a 1995 *Daidalos* article by Jan Pieper, the Palladian Bridge marked the literal transition from rigid, formal garden design to the new, liberated artistry of the landscape park. In its metaphoric role, the Palladian Bridge—punctuating the vista as it does at the edge of a valley called the Elysian Fields—evokes the rational order of Palladio no doubt to reassure the estate's noble occupants of their own safe passage and final reward.

Although reconstructed many times, the wooden bridge over the Brenta River in Bassano del Grappa, Italy, is true to Palladio's 1569 design. The original bridge stood for 178 years, testifying to the fitness of its design.

| Crossing Octagon Lake | Designer/Engineer unknown | Completed c. 1744 | Length 92 feet/28 meters | Materials stone | Type arch |

*[Iron Bridge] is designed in the spirit of masonry, while the detailing of the members is unmistakably that of contemporary timber construction.*
—Robert Maguire and Peter Matthews, "The Ironbridge at Coalbrookdale," Architectural Association Journal, 1958

The bridge, a beautiful object in a sublime natural setting, has been the object of artistic pilgrimage since its completion, inspiring etchings such as this one published in 1786.

# Iron Bridge

The Iron Bridge at Coalbrookdale is a seminal bridge. It did not represent a technological breakthrough or have a revolutionary design. It was not the first bridge to use iron as a building material. However, as the first major structure to be constructed entirely of iron, it endures as the earliest portent of the fundamental changes that would be brought about by the Industrial Revolution, which originated in Great Britain in the late eighteenth century. Two innovations of this new age, the steam engine and iron—plentiful, cheap, far stronger than wood, more flexible than stone—triggered interconnected economic, technical, and social developments that would alter the world irrevocably.

The Severn meanders through the picturesque town of Coalbrookdale in Shropshire, where iron was first smelted with coke. To replace a ferry crossing there, Thomas Farnolls Pritchard drew up a plan for a cast-iron arch bridge composed of five nearly semicircular ribs supporting a 24-foot (7-meter)-wide iron roadway. It was Abraham Darby III, a third-generation master ironworker, who suggested to Pritchard that iron would be a stronger and less weighty alternative to traditional stone or wood. There is some dispute among architectural historians as to who actually drew up the final plans for the bridge, as Pritchard died shortly after the meeting at which the bridge was commissioned. In any case, Darby took control of the construction process.

"This Bridge Was Cast At Coalbrook Dale And Erected In The Year MDCCLXXIX." So reads the inscription on the bridge's main outer ribs. Nearly 400 tons (363 tonnes) of cast iron, some 800 separate castings in all, were floated down the river and assembled in the course of three short months. Completed in 1779, the bridge has a 100-foot (30.5-meter) span and a total length of 196 feet (60 meters).

Little engineering expertise was applied in the actual construction; with a few modifications for the different material, the techniques used in building Iron Bridge were the same as those used in building timber or masonry bridges. No bolts were used in joining the metal, and, as in timber bridges, the sections of the bridge are held together with screws.

Iron's potential was not yet understood. But when Iron Bridge proved to be the only bridge that survived the Severn River flood of 1795, Thomas Telford, the unparalleled engineer of that era, took notice. He recognized the superior strength of iron and from then on worked only in that material.

In 1934 Iron Bridge was declared an "ancient monument" and closed to vehicular traffic. After years of neglect, the bridge is now the centerpiece of a village-wide complex of museums that celebrate Coalbrookdale's distinct contribution to the iron industry. Iron Bridge remains not only a monument to the innovative thinking preceding the Industrial Revolution but also a poignant indicator of the rapid progress of engineering technology since then.

The timber-like detailing of the iron members can be seen clearly: dovetails, mortises, wedges, and screws appear in profusion.

| Crossing | Severn River | Designer/Engineer | Abraham Darby III, Thomas Farnolls Pritchard | Completed | 1779 First large-scale cast-iron bridge | Length: span | 100 feet/30.5 meters | Materials | iron | Type | arch |

*I heard him then, for I had just
Completed my design
To keep the Menai Bridge from rust
By boiling it in wine.*

—Lewis Carroll, Through the Looking Glass, 1872

The wrought-iron chains, replaced in 1942 with steel chains, were treated with boiled linseed oil and dried to prevent rust.

Menai Suspension Bridge, Wales

When Ireland was linked politically with Britain in 1801, a reliable mail connection between London and Dublin became imperative. Standing in the way were the notoriously unpredictable waters of the Menai Strait and the equally resistant residents of Caernarfon, who were vehemently opposed to a bridge from the first talk of such a plan two decades earlier because their livelihoods were based on shipping. Expensive international conflicts, such as the American Revolution and the Napoleonic Wars, slowed construction as well. Over the years various proposals, including cast-iron arch designs by John Rennie and Thomas Telford, did not materialize.

**Thomas Telford (1757–1834), a self-taught Scottish engineer, was unequaled in his masterly and prolific construction of roads, canals, harbors, and bridges. He was one of the first to understand civil engineering as an art separate from architecture, and he articulated its goals as efficiency in materials, economy, and appearance—standards that remain today. He built many monuments of eighteenth-century engineering, most of which still stand, including Pont-y-Cysyllte, Wales (1805); Craigellachie Bridge, Scotland (1815); and the Conway River Bridge, Wales (1826).**

Finally, in 1818 Thomas Telford (1757–1834) began work on what is considered by most to be his masterpiece, the Menai Suspension Bridge. Telford, then at the peak of a mighty building career, was assisted by Captain Samuel Brown, whose interest in ship rigging eventually led to his designing an early suspension bridge, the Union Bridge over the Tweed in 1820. Together Telford and Brown executed hundreds of load tests to satisfy themselves of the strength of wrought iron. Both were undoubtedly aware of the work of an American, James Finley, who had published his "Patent Chain Bridge" in *The Port Folio* (1810) and would eventually build some forty, albeit small and crude, suspension bridges.

Construction on the Menai Strait Bridge began in 1819. When the masonry towers were completed in 1824, there was "breathless silence" as the first chain was floated out and linked to the chain hanging from the Caernarfon pier. Ultimately, sixteen huge chains would be suspended from the two piers, creating a dramatic curve and the necessary leverage to support the unprecedented center span of 579 feet (176 meters). Four hundred and forty-four vertical suspension rods hanging from the chains supported the roadway.

Telford's revolutionary bridge design would inform all suspension bridges to follow. His achievement is even more noteworthy when one considers that the bridge was built twenty years before the steam engine was fully developed. Telford harnessed manpower, horsepower, and the tides themselves to bring the bridge, stone by stone, link by link, to completion.

Impressive limestone arches, four on the Anglesey side and three on the Welsh, lead to the central span between the two 153-foot (47-meter)-tall towers. After the cornerstone was laid, three hundred men battled the weather and the tides for four years to build the stone approaches. Telford himself had begun as a stone mason.

*Telford was the first civil engineer consciously to move away from the old canons of architectural taste....He was thinking all the time about appearance and landscape and form but, for Telford, the possibility for beauty must come internally from what the technical and economic constraints suggest.*
—David Billington, The Tower and the Bridge, 1983

# Menai Suspension Bridge

| Crossing | Menai Strait | Designer/Engineer | Thomas Telford | Completed | 1826 | Span | 579 feet/176 meters | Materials | wrought iron, limestone | Type | suspension |
| --- | --- | --- | --- | --- | --- | --- | --- | --- | --- | --- | --- |
| | | | | | First major suspension bridge; longest suspension bridge 1826–1834 | | | | | | |

London Bridge was relocated to Lake Havasu City, Arizona.

*What price do you offer for an antique bridge whose principal assets are legend, architectural beauty, quality granite, and a song handed down from generation to generation reporting the bridge's antecedent is falling down?*
— Roger Johnson, Old Bridge, New City, 1981

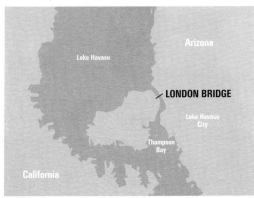

*[London Bridge] stands as one of the strangest monuments to our sense of possession over purpose.*

—Henry Petroski, Engineers of Dreams, 1995

# London Bridge

In 1958 Robert P. McCulloch, a successful American entrepreneur, flew over the Arizona desert in search of a test site for outboard motors. He spotted an abandoned Army Air Corps site that fronted Lake Havasu, a 45-mile (72-kilometer)-long reservoir formed when the Parker Dam was completed in 1938. Instead of barren scrub, McCulloch envisioned a planned community that would support his various business ventures. Soon joined in his enterprise by C. V. Wood, a master planner who had previously worked on the development of Disneyland, McCulloch created Lake Havasu City in 1963.

By 1968 Lake Havasu City was thriving. At the same time, London Bridge was sinking, a victim of the Thames's porous subsoil, its own great weight, and heavy foot and vehicular traffic. John Rennie's last great work, the five-arched granite bridge was one of many to cross the Thames at that site, over the centuries becoming steeped in lore and legend that far exceeded Rennie's straightforward design.

At the insistence of one Ivan F. Luckin, the city of London was persuaded to mount an international campaign, directed primarily at Americans, to sell the bridge. Fortunately, McCulloch was in the market for a bridge to span a channel that had yet to be dug to eliminate a blockage in one part of Lake Havasu. London, maddeningly, would not name a price, preferring instead to field bids, indicating that decorum and good intentions would count as much as money.

McCulloch and Wood determined that the cost of dismantling and shipping the granite blocks of the bridge would run about $1.2 million, a figure they doubled; assuming other prospective buyers would come up with the same formula, they added $1,000 for each year of McCulloch's life. Even before their winning bid of $2,460,000 was formally announced, British headlines read, "London Bridge Falls to the Apaches."

It took three years to dismantle, ship, and reconstruct the bridge in its desert home. Under the supervision of Robert Beresford, a British civil engineer, a new steel-reinforced concrete core was built over the desert and then faced with the imported masonry. The construction itself was accomplished by forty men in a year and a half; the original bridge, in contrast, had required a crew of eight hundred men who labored for seven years and suffered forty fatalities. When the reconstruction was completed, a channel was dredged beneath it. It was dedicated in 1971.

Although it has been said that McCulloch "bought a bridge he didn't need for a river he didn't have," the relocation of the London Bridge was ingenious, granting an unknown desert oasis an instant cultural identity and conferring immortality on an otherwise architecturally ordinary bridge.

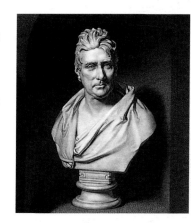

John Rennie (1761–1821), one of the great bridge builders of the nineteenth century, drew up plans for the London Bridge in 1821; his design was eventually executed under the supervision of his son John.

Old London Bridge, built under the direction of Peter of Colechurch, was completed in 1209 and stood for over six hundred years. It replaced a series of timber spans that had either burned or collapsed, most notably in 1014, when the Vikings pulled it down while it was full of Danish soldiers—a feat immortalized in the rhyme "London Bridge Is Falling Down."

| Crossing | Thames; Lake Havasu | Designer | John Rennie | Completed | 1831; rebuilt, 1971 | Length | London: 1005 feet/306 meters / Arizona: 952 feet/290 meters | Material | granite | Type | arch |

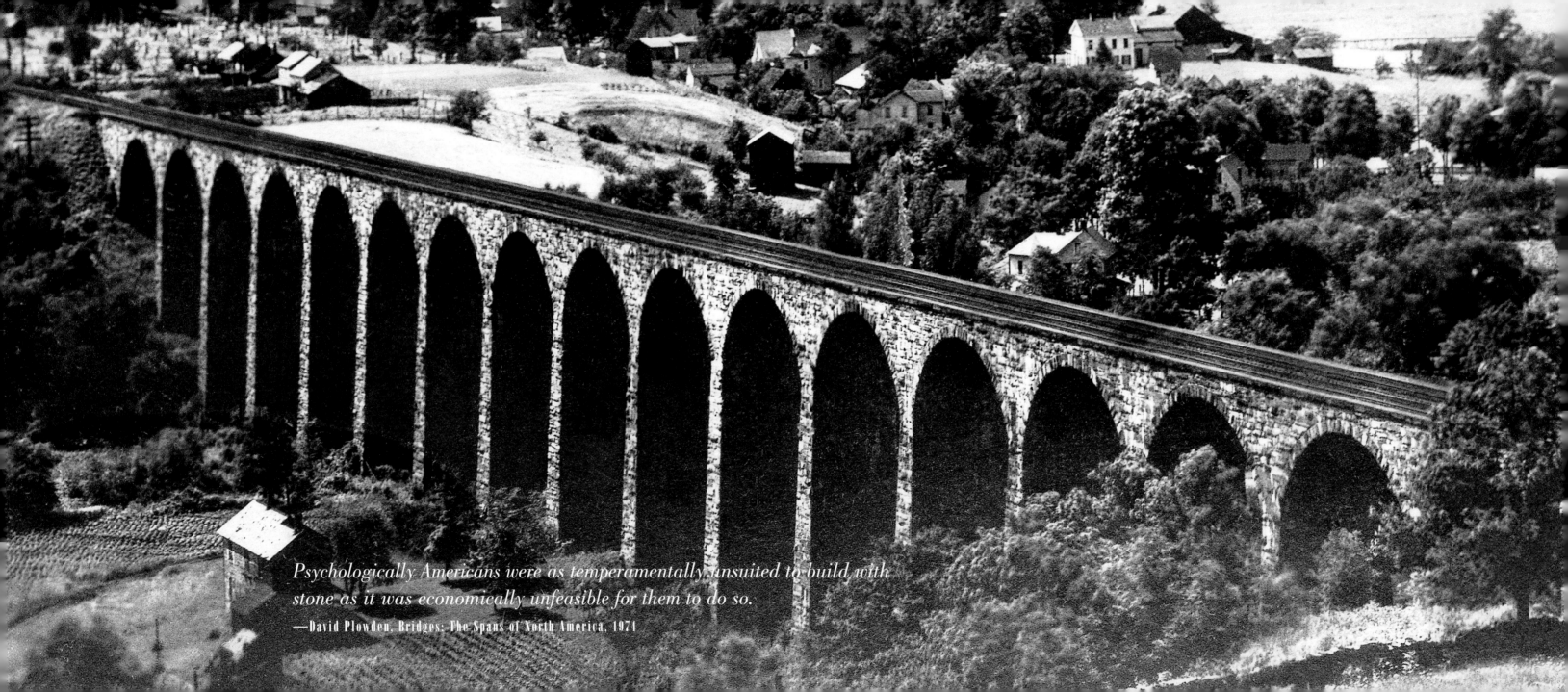

*Psychologically Americans were as temperamentally unsuited to build with stone as it was economically unfeasible for them to do so.*
—David Plowden, *Bridges: The Spans of North America*, 1974

# Starrucca Viaduct

The 19-by-40-foot (6-by-12-meter) footings for the thirteen full-height piers were concrete slabs made of cement from the Rosendale works in Ulster County, New York, representing the first documented use of that material in America.

The most precious commodity in eighteenth-century America—a new nation impatient to expand its frontiers with canals and railroads—was time. Stone bridges, though exceedingly strong and permanent, required time, and lots of it, to quarry, shape, and individually fit each piece. David Plowden notes in his classic illustrated survey, *Bridges*, that few of America's rail lines were able to justify the high cost of stone bridges, an observation borne out by the fact that prior to 1850 only four significant masonry bridges had been built. These four viaducts—the Carrollton (1829), Thomas (1835), Canton (1835), and Starrucca (1848)—represent the finest examples of masonry construction in North America. The largest, the Starrucca Viaduct, is a monumental structure made graceful by its simple, slender proportions.

Its builder, the New York and Erie Railroad Company, was one of the largest economic enterprises of the time. It was incorporated in 1832 to build a line that by 1851 would stretch 484 miles (774 kilometers) from Piermont on the Hudson River to Dunkirk on Lake Erie—a route determined by political, not economic, considerations. New York State approved the company's charter on the condition that the line stay far from the Erie Canal, which ran from Buffalo to Albany; canal interests were powerful enough at that time to force the railroad to build its route through difficult terrain along New York's southern border. Although a number of surveys were made and abandoned before the final route was selected, the chosen route had its own obstacles. The biggest one, the deep valley at the Starrucca Creek at Lanesboro, Pennsylvania, brought work to a standstill in 1844 while engineers decided what to do.

Julius W. Adams, from a family of prominent railroad builders and the supervising engineer of the New York and Erie line, designed the 1,040-foot (317-meter)-long viaduct that would span Starrucca Creek. He was assisted by his brother-in-law, James P. Kirkwood, a Scottish engineer who had the experience needed to accomplish a masonry project of this magnitude and, it appears, the confidence as well (when asked if he could complete the job by 1848, Kirkwood is said to have replied, "I can... provided you don't care how much it may cost"). Construction finally started in 1847.

The Starrucca Viaduct is composed of seventeen semi-circular arches, each with a span of 51 feet (16 meters), which rise on tapered piers 110 feet (34 meters) above the valley floor. The pier bases and roadway were made of concrete. The rest of the structure was constructed from local bluestone and brick. Kirkwood's boast proved prophetic: the final cost of the lavish Starrucca Viaduct, completed in one year by eight hundred men, was $320,000—the most expensive railroad bridge built to that time.

Both the time and the money were well spent, however. On December 9, 1848, the first locomotive crossed the double-track viaduct and it has been in use ever since. The New York and Erie Railroad did not fare as well. In the 1860s, as a pawn in a series of underhanded financial schemes, the line was known as "the Scarlet Woman of Wall Street." In the 1870s it suffered its fourth and final bankruptcy. Reorganized a number of times, the line emerged in 1960 as the Erie Lackawanna Railway Company, only to become bankrupt again in 1972. The line was taken over by Conrail in 1976.

| Crossing | Starrucca Creek | Designer/Engineer | Julius W. Adams and James P. Kirkwood | Completed | 1848 | Length | 1,040 feet/317 meters | Materials | masonry | Type | arch viaduct |

When completed in 1866, the Cincinnati Bridge over the Ohio River had the longest span (1,057 feet; 322 meters) in the world. Roebling's design was executed by his son, Washington. As noted by bridge authority Eric DeLony, this project would nurture the father-son relationship that proved critical to completing the Brooklyn Bridge sixteen years later. Between 1895 and 1899 the Cincinnati Bridge was strengthened with steel stiffening trusses and additional cables.

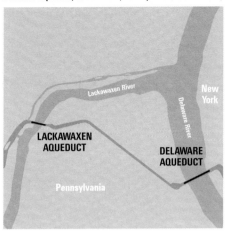

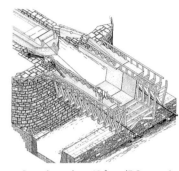

Canal barges traveled over the Delaware Aqueduct via a 19-foot (5.8-meter)-wide wooden water trough, as shown in this isometric view.

The Delaware Aqueduct is the sole survivor of the four suspension aqueducts built in America by John A. Roebling between 1848 and 1850. Though not the world's first suspension bridge—notable precedents built on both sides of the Atlantic include James Finley's Jacob's Creek Bridge in Pennsylvania (1801), Thomas Telford's Menai Suspension Bridge in Wales (1826; see pages 36–37), Joseph Chaley's Grand Pont Suspendu in Switzerland (1834), and Charles Ellet's Fairmount Bridge in Pennsylvania (1841) and Wheeling Bridge in West Virginia (1849)—it is the oldest wire-cable suspension bridge still standing that retains most of its original structure. It is also the earliest extant example of the type of bridge that would secure John Roebling's place in history.

Coal from northeastern Pennsylvania was transported on boats pulled through waterways on the Lackawaxen, Delaware, and Hudson rivers before reaching its final destination, the profitable markets of New York City. By the mid-nineteenth century, this method of shipping was deemed too slow and unreliable in the face of increasing competition from the burgeoning rail system. In 1847 R. F. Lord, chief engineer of the Delaware and Hudson Canal Company, accepted Roebling's unconventional but apparently economical design for two suspended aqueducts to span the Lackawaxen and Delaware rivers.

The design of the Delaware Aqueduct consists of a waterway, or flume, flanked by tow paths on either side. The weight of the water is carried by two continuous main cables, each 8.5 inches (21.6 cm) in diameter and composed of 2,150 wires. The cables are draped from cast-iron saddles mounted on squat masonry towers, forming four spans with lengths ranging from 131 to 142 feet (40 to 43 meters). The Lackawaxen Aqueduct, a half mile away, was constructed in a nearly identical manner. Both structurally and operationally, the aqueducts were an unqualified success.

John Augustus Roebling (1806–1869), the father of the modern suspension bridge, was gifted with a brilliant analytical mind, inexhaustible curiosity, and an iron will. German born, Roebling studied architecture at Berlin's Royal Polytechnic Institute, as well as philosophy under Hegel, whose doctrine of self-realization proved a powerful influence. He emigrated to the United States in 1831 to establish an agrarian community in Saxonburg, Pennsylvania. While working as a canal surveyor, Roebling witnessed an accident caused by a snapped hemp cable and had a breakthrough revelation about the superior strength of wire rope—a discovery that would shape his Promethean career. By 1845 he had completed two prototypical suspension bridges—the Pittsburgh Aqueduct over the Allegheny Canal and the Monongahela Bridge in Pittsburgh—that would inform all his future designs.

In 1898 the last boat passed through the Delaware Aqueduct, which was subsequently converted into a vehicular bridge. In 1980 it was acquired by the National Park Service, which has re-created the original appearance of its superstructure.

# Delaware Aqueduct

*We may affirm absolutely that nothing great in the world has been accomplished without passion.*
—G.W.F. Hegel, Philosophy of History, 1832

| Crossing | Delaware River | Designer/Engineer | John A. Roebling | Completed | 1849 / Oldest Suspension Bridge in America | Length | 535 feet/163 meters | Materials | iron, masonry | Type | suspension |

In an 1889 paper on American railroad bridges, respected engineer Theodore Cooper (1839–1919) documented the loads exerted by trains, concluding with a discussion of bridge failure. He called for the careful calculation of stresses, material testing, and inspection but added that a bridge's stability was more reliant on the engineer's instincts than "merely upon a theory of stresses." His words would come back to haunt him eighteen years later, when he played a role in the most famous bridge collapse in history.

By the end of the nineteenth century, with the expansion of the railroad, bridge collapses were noted with increasing regularity and hysteria. Well-qualified scholars still debate how many bridges failed—some say one in four; others, one in four thousand—though without adequate documentation, the actual numbers cannot be ascertained. Many collapses were attributable to causes other than structural inadequacies, including train derailment, fire, and flooding.

Truss designer Ithiel Town's slogan, "Build it by the mile and cut it off by the yard," describes the attitude and methodology of the many bridge companies competing

Québec Bridge Collapse, 1907

to build more and longer railroad bridges. Though this climate fostered the development of an economical and practical style of metal truss bridge, it was also rife with corruption—skimping on materials and on the review of the bridge's technical design was not uncommon. Bridges designed by highly esteemed engineers also collapsed, however, indicating the pervasive role of human error in failure.

Robert Stephenson's Dee Bridge (1845) across the River Dee in England—the longest metal truss built to that date—provides the first instance of a metal bridge collapse that might have been avoided if information known at the time had been made available to engineers. Success with earlier truss bridges led to the progressive increase in their span length without considering the additional structural needs that the extra length imposed. The bridge girders buckled under these unconsidered stresses and fell on May 24, 1847, claiming five lives.

On December 28, 1879, Thomas Bouch's Tay Bridge over Scotland's Firth of Tay went down in a gale with the loss of seventy-five souls. When completed in 1876, the rail bridge had been hailed as an "engineering triumph" and earned a knighthood for Bouch. Later found to be fatally complacent, Bouch had relied on outdated data that neglected the dynamic forces of violent gusts.

In the 1907 collapse of the Québec Bridge over the St. Lawrence River in Canada, an ill-fated combination of technical error, corporate parsimony, miscommunication, and professional hubris caused the deaths of seventy-five workmen. The Québec Bridge Company had hired Theodore Cooper of New York to consult on the Pennsylvania-based Phoenix Bridge Company's cantilever design, which Cooper had selected as the "best and cheapest" of those submitted; as is often the case, Québec wanted to spend as little as possible. Cooper increased the length of the bridge's main span from 1,600 to 1,800 feet (488 to 549 meters) without recalculation of stresses. When asked about the soundness of his work, Cooper replied, "There is nobody competent to criticize us."

By August 1907, when the south arm of the bridge had been cantilevered out about 600 feet (183 meters), the discovery that the steel chords were bent was

followed by three weeks of debate about *when* they were bent and not *why*. Cooper, who never visited the site when the superstructure was under construction, sent a telegram on August 27 ordering the work stopped until the bent chord issue was resolved. The crucial telegram was ignored, either undelivered or unread, and work continued until August 29, when the bridge collapsed from its faulty design. Ironically, its replacement would also collapse in 1916, taking eleven lives.

The Québec disaster influenced the development of suspension spans for long distances. Yet the suspension bridge over Tacoma Narrows collapsed in 1940 because the designer failed to consider aerodynamic forces (see page 85). In 1970 two bridges of a new type, the steel box girder, went down, one in Wales and the other in Australia.

A 1977 report by Paul Sibly and Alastair Walker notes a thirty-year cycle of bridge failures and their shared characteristics. Each of the bridges involved was a new type of bridge (trussed girder, truss, cantilever, suspension, and box girder) that was being developed in response to the collapse of an earlier type of bridge.

Engineer and author Henry Petroski extends Sibly and Walker's findings by thirty years and theorizes that the next collapse might involve a cable-stayed design, the newest type of bridge.

While human error will always be a variable in bridge design, improvements in other areas—more reliable materials, expanded technical knowledge, wind testing, computer technology, and the growing recognition that failures, having the most to teach about successful design, should be documented and shared—have taken some of the uncertainty out of bridge engineering.

# Catastrophe

*The bridge seemed to be among the things that last forever; it was unthinkable that it should break.*
—Thornton Wilder, The Bridge of San Luis Rey, 1927

Inset: 1964 Collapse of the Million Dollar Bridge, Alaska
Background: Tay Bridge Collapse, 1879

Each of the four lions at the approach piers are 25 feet (8 meters) long and 12 feet (4 meters) high. The original plan was to have a massive figure of Britannia on the center tower but the cost was prohibitive.

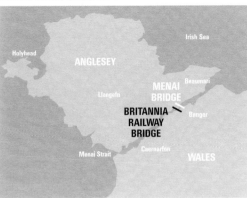

*The tubes filled my head. I went to bed with them and I got up with them.*

—Robert Stephenson, in Eric de Maré, The Bridges of Britain, 1975

# Britannia Railway Bridge

In 1838, twelve years after Thomas Telford erected his revolutionary suspension bridge over the Menai Strait in Wales, Robert Stephenson (1803–1859) designed a second crossing. Stephenson, the son of George Stephenson, "the Father of the Railways," was commissioned to build a bridge exclusively for railroad traffic one mile west of Telford's. Because Stephenson had to span the strait without impeding the passage of ships through it, an arched bridge—which would have required a temporary support in the middle of the strait—was not an option.

With William Fairbairn, a pioneering metallurgist, engineer, and shipbuilder, Stephenson experimented with iron, the first manmade material that would revolutionize building in the nineteenth century. Serendipitously, they heard of an iron ship that had accidently become suspended in air during its launch without damage to the hull. This information gave them confidence in their novel plan to span the strait with a tubular bridge of riveted wrought iron. (Stephenson's courage in developing this new technology is all the greater when one learns that an earlier bridge he had designed at Chester had recently collapsed, killing five people, an accident for which he blamed himself.)

The bridge would consist of two independent box tunnels, or tubes, set side by side with a total length of 1,511 feet (461 meters), supported by three monumental limestone towers. The central 221-foot (67-meter)-high tower was anchored on Britannia Island, a small midstream island. At first, the tubes were to be supported by chains suspended from the towers, but Fairbairn discovered that if the tubes' vertical walls were reinforced with stiffeners they could support their own weight without supplementary chains. Stephenson's design is unresolved: visually the towers appear ungainly, perpetually in wait for the unnecessary suspension chains.

Stephenson laid the foundation stone on April 10, 1846, and on March 5, 1850, escorted the first train through the pioneering tube. The second tube had not yet been put into place, and until it was, a man accompanied every train through the tunnel to prevent wrecks.

The bridge was stable, withstanding the loads that rumbled its length for over a century. In the end, two boys caused its demise. On May 23, 1970, while looking for a bat roost, the youngsters climbed on top of the bridge, which was protected by a wooden canopy, and dropped a flare when they left. The roof and then the entire bridge caught fire, damaging the tubes beyond repair. The bridge was rebuilt using arches—ironically, given Stephenson's strict parameters in 1838—and a roadway was added as well.

The greatest obstacle in building the bridge was the daunting prospect of guiding each of the 1,800-ton (1,633-tonne) central sections 100 feet (30 meters) up a vertical groove cut into the piers, seen here under construction. Stephenson handled this problem with characteristic ingenuity, floating the girders on pontoons—this time the strait's extremes tides were an ally—and raising them with hydraulic lifts.

To accommodate "railway mania" during the first half of the nineteenth century, the number of bridges in Britain doubled from 30,000 to 60,000. The bridge's gigantic iron girders, seen here in section, were 30 feet (9 meters) high and nearly 15 feet (5 meters) wide. They were the prototype of the modern steel box girder.

| Crossing | Menai Strait | Designer/Engineer | Robert Stephenson | Completed | 1850 | Length | center spans: 480 feet/146 meters | Materials | wrought iron, limestone | Type | iron girder |
| --- | --- | --- | --- | --- | --- | --- | --- | --- | --- | --- | --- |
| | | | | | | | end spans: 230 feet/70 meters | | | | |

The interior of the Bridgeport Covered Bridge reveals the additional arch that was needed to carry the unprecedented span.

Cornish-Windsor Covered Bridge, Cornish, New Hampshire—Windsor, Vermont

*People don't build covered bridges very often these days. And I think the most important decision that was made was to restore this bridge, to strengthen this bridge and in doing so strengthen this wonderful tradition of craftsmanship, of beauty, of what New England is all about.*

—Madeleine M. Kunin, Governor of Vermont, at the reopening of the Cornish-Windsor Covered Bridge, 1989

# Cornish-Windsor Covered Bridge

December 8, 1989, was a cold day in Cornish, New Hampshire. The temperature was 20 degrees Fahrenheit and the wind made it seem even colder. Still, more than a thousand people showed up for the reopening of the Cornish-Windsor Covered Bridge.

Straddling the Connecticut River, the bridge connects Cornish with the Vermont town of Windsor. Several earlier bridges on that spot were lost to floods. The present bridge was built in 1866 by James Tasker and Bela Fletcher, two local men who, though uneducated, successfully used their rule-of-thumb design experience to build a lasting truss structure (see pages 60–61). On the National Register of Historic Places, the bridge is celebrated for being the longest two-lane covered bridge in America.

On July 2, 1987, New Hampshire officials had to shut it down for safety reasons. The closing created a tremendous inconvenience for businesses on both sides of the river, which had come to depend on the 460-foot (140-meter) span. Thus began one of the most extensive covered-bridge restoration projects in recent history. Over the next twenty-eight months, close to $5 million was spent on repairs. As most of the bridge is technically within New Hampshire's borders, that state picked up the lion's share of the tab —a fact that Vermont's governor gleefully noted at the reopening ceremony.

The Cornish-Windsor bridge was one of thousands of covered wooden bridges built in America in the nineteenth century. The first covered bridge, the so-called Permanent Bridge in Philadelphia, opened in 1805. The pony-tailed Timothy Palmer of Newburyport, Massachusetts, is credited with designing the 550-foot (168-meter) bridge, which spanned the Schuylkill River. Interestingly enough, Palmer's original design didn't have a roof. He was encouraged to top the bridge by a judge who oversaw the six-year building project. Palmer agreed, predicting that the Permanent Bridge could last as long as 30 to 40 years covered, as opposed to 10 or 12 uncovered. It ultimately survived 45 years. After it opened, covered bridges became the rule, not the exception.

Considered a "wonder of the world," the Upper Ferry bridge soon came to be called the Colossus at Philadelphia or simply the Colossus. A number of images of it on old prints such as this one have survived.

But some Philadelphians weren't content with Palmer's bridge. In 1812 a second span across the Schuylkill was completed in Upper Ferry. Lewis Wernag, a German immigrant, was hired to build the bridge. His design for what became known as the Colossus was so bold that many thought it was doomed to fail. With a span of 340 feet (104 meters), it was the second longest single-span covered bridge in the world. The riverbanks were jammed with people on the day the supports were taken away. They wanted to see if a bridge that long could stand. It did, immediately placing Wernag in the annals of bridge building.

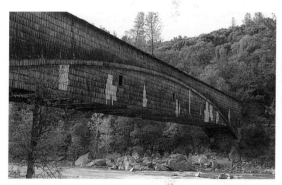

The 233-foot (71-meter) Bridgeport Covered Bridge (1862), the longest single-span covered bridge in the United States, was built across California's Yuba River to access a silver mine. An extra, strengthening arch that was superimposed on the bridge's truss structure is reflected in the exterior shingle siding.

| Crossing | Connecticut River | Builders | James Tasker and Bela Fletcher | Completed | 1866 Longest two-lane covered bridge in the United States | Length | 460 feet/140 meters | Materials | wood | Type | Town lattice truss |

*Whipple's book and innovations mark a fundamental change in bridge design from a craft tradition to an engineering profession.*

—Eric DeLony, Landmark American Bridges, 1993

For many years the oldest surviving metal truss bridge, the Fink Through-Truss Bridge (1858) in Hamden, New Jersey, collapsed in 1978 when it was hit by an automobile.

Henzey's Wrought-Iron Arch Bridge (1869) in Wanamakers, Pennsylvania, by Joseph G. Henzey is a rare example of a prefabricated metal-truss design.

The Bollman Truss Bridge (1869), on an abandoned spur of the Baltimore and Ohio Railroad in Savage, Maryland, is a unique suspension and truss hybrid patented in 1852 by Bollman.

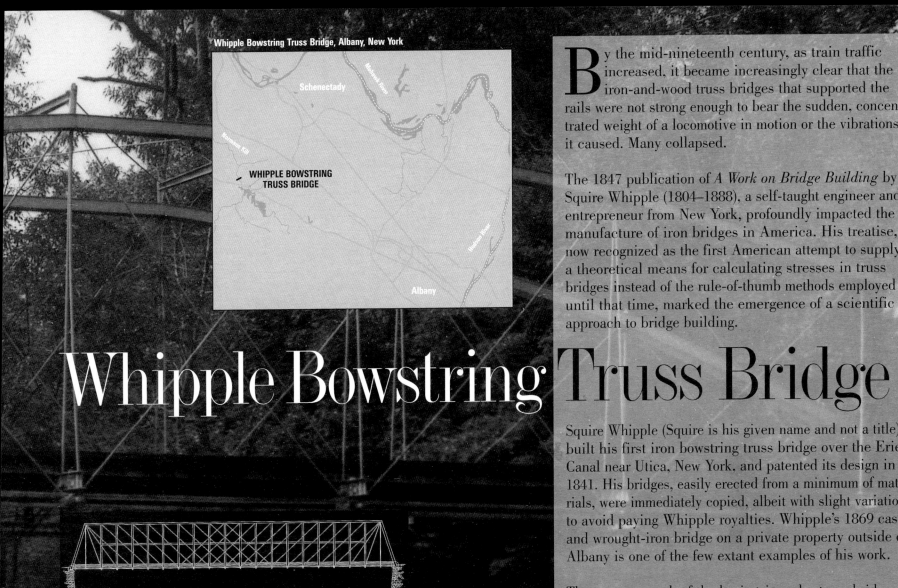

WHIPPLE BOWSTRING
TRUSS BRIDGE

Schenectady

Albany

# Whipple Bowstring Truss Bridge

The Laughery Creek Bridge (1878), a rare triple-intersection Pratt truss located near Aurora, Indiana, has a remarkable 302-foot (127-meter) span.

By the mid-nineteenth century, as train traffic increased, it became increasingly clear that the iron-and-wood truss bridges that supported the rails were not strong enough to bear the sudden, concentrated weight of a locomotive in motion or the vibrations it caused. Many collapsed.

The 1847 publication of *A Work on Bridge Building* by Squire Whipple (1804–1888), a self-taught engineer and entrepreneur from New York, profoundly impacted the manufacture of iron bridges in America. His treatise, now recognized as the first American attempt to supply a theoretical means for calculating stresses in truss bridges instead of the rule-of-thumb methods employed until that time, marked the emergence of a scientific approach to bridge building.

Squire Whipple (Squire is his given name and not a title) built his first iron bowstring truss bridge over the Erie Canal near Utica, New York, and patented its design in 1841. His bridges, easily erected from a minimum of materials, were immediately copied, albeit with slight variations to avoid paying Whipple royalties. Whipple's 1869 cast-and wrought-iron bridge on a private property outside of Albany is one of the few extant examples of his work.

The great strength of the basic triangular truss bridge gave rise to many variations utilizing different combinations of cast and wrought iron, the more prominent of which were named for their developers, including Wendel Bollman (1814–1884), Albert Fink (1827–1897), and Thomas Pratt (1812–1875). Many more of these inventive filigreed-iron structures were patented and aggressively marketed by anonymous entrepreneurial craftsmen who provided a young America with the bridges she needed to expand west.

By the mid-1870s the myriad truss designs marketed before and after the Civil War evolved into what became known as the American Standard. Descended from Pratt's truss of 1850, the American Standard was utilized on both sides of the Atlantic and characterized by the use of prefabricated cast-iron sections that could be rapidly assembled on site by semiskilled labor.

Of the hundreds of metal trusses built between 1840 and 1880, only a handful survived; those that were not destroyed in the Civil War fell victim to the scrap metal drives of the world wars, or were torn down and replaced. According to Eric DeLony, chief of the Historic American Engineering Record—an organization dedicated to the preservation of America's built environment in drawings and photographs, including those reproduced here— another reason why so few early metal truss bridges remain is that "they are not recognized by the public, preservationists, or the engineering profession as being as significant as the more monumental Brooklyn or Golden Gate suspension bridges, or the quaint and nostalgic stone arches or wooden covered spans." The pioneering metal bridges of the Civil War era, America's rarest artifacts, are in danger of extinction.

| Crossing | near Normans Kill Ravine | Designer/Engineer | Squire Whipple; Constructed by Simon DeGraff | Completed | 1869 | Length | 110 feet/33.5 meters | Materials | cast and wrought iron | Type | truss |

A supremely talented, indefatigable, and confident engineer, Eads
is best described by his famous
question: "Must we admit that
because a thing has never been
done it can never be?"

*It was typical of Eads that he had never before built a bridge. His*
*technical daring and founded on a unique and intimate knowledge*
—Howard Miller, The Eads Bridge, 1979

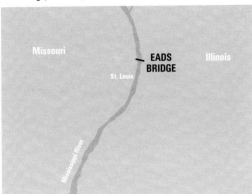

# Eads Bridge

To meet Eads's exacting standards, Flad designed a machine capable of detecting minute variations in the steel's measurements and tensile strength.

*career had been a succession of bold innovations marked by of the Mississippi River.*

Steamboats traveling up and down the mighty Mississippi had brought St. Louis great prosperity. By 1860 however, St. Louis was losing business to Chicago, which was served by eleven rail lines and had "overturned the sovereignty of the rivers." Stranded by the very river that had put it on the map, St. Louis had no alternative but to build a bridge across the Mississippi.

James Buchanan Eads (1820–1887) ultimately triumphed with a proposal for a bridge like no other: a three-arched span that would be taller and longer than anything yet built in the United States. The bridge would be made of steel, a new material that had never been used on the scale proposed. Most radically of all, Eads had never built a bridge.

Eads's knowledge of the capricious Mississippi was unsurpassed. He first got to know the river as a steamboat clerk. Steamboats and their cargo regularly sank, victims of fire, boiler explosions, or river debris. To recover this sunken treasure, Eads began a salvage business. Equipped with a jerry-built diving bell, Eads kept at this hazardous work, literally walking the turbulent river bottom, sometimes for miles. Along the way, he built a fortune and a national reputation as the river's leading expert; in 1863, at President Lincoln's request, he designed a fleet of ironclad gunboats to defend the Mississippi during the Civil War.

Construction of the bridge began in 1867. The spans were built by extending the halves of each arch outward, while supporting them with guy wires, until they met in the middle. Riding on the closure of the first span by September 19, 1873, was a half-million-dollar loan.

September's extreme heat had so expanded the metal arches that they could not be joined. Panicked, Eads's chief assistant, Henry Flad, tried to shrink the metal by packing it in 60 tons (54 tonnes) of ice, to no avail. But the foresighted Eads had developed a means of raising the arches so they could be closed with the insertion of a screw mechanism. On September 17 the arches were successfully closed. The whole of Eads's heroic endeavor was chronicled by Calvin Woodward in his classic text, *The History of the St. Louis Bridge* (1881).

The joining of Missouri and Illinois was celebrated with a gala on July 4, 1874. The bridge was much praised: Louis Sullivan called it "sensational and tectonic," while Walt Whitman extolled the "perfection and beauty unsurpassable" of its structure. A plaque on the bridge simply read: "The Mississippi discovered by Marquette, 1673; spanned by Captain Eads, 1874."

Less than a year later, the bridge was bankrupt—over-capitalized and underused. Eads was not present in 1878 when his visionary structure was sold at public auction. Exactly one century after its opening, the last train crossed it. The bridge became a dingy haunt for pigeons and derelicts. Today the Eads Bridge stands in the shadow of Eero Saarinen's Gateway Arch, unnoticed by most drivers, who are perhaps unaware they are crossing an American original.

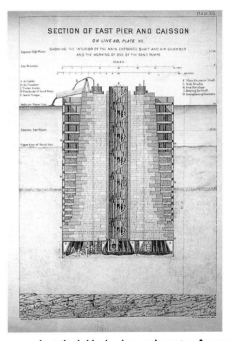

Eads used pneumatic caissons to plant the bridge's piers underwater. As seen in this cutaway detail, the caisson's open, knifelike bottom cut into the riverbed. Workmen, operating in claustrophobic conditions and breathing compressed air, shoveled buckets of debris, which were hauled out on pulleys. Others built stone foundations on the caisson's closed top, forcing it still deeper. Fourteen men died from the bends, or caisson's disease, which is caused by a too-rapid decompression.

| Crossing | Mississippi River | Designer/Engineer | James Buchanan Eads | Completed | 1874 | Length | 1,524 feet/480 meters | Materials | steel | Type | arch |
|---|---|---|---|---|---|---|---|---|---|---|---|
| | | | | | First major bridge constructed of steel | | | | | | |

*The work which is likely to be our most durable monument, and to convey some knowledge of us to the most remote posterity, is a work of bare utility; not a shrine, not a fortress, not a palace, but a bridge.*

—Montgomery Schuyler, "The Bridge as a Monument," Harpers Weekly, 1883

Anyone crossing the promenade experiences the uncanny sensation of observing the bridge while simultaneously becoming part of its enveloping structure.

BROOKLYN BRIDGE

# Brooklyn Bridge

At the stroke of midnight on May 23, 1883—after President Chester Arthur, Governor Grover Cleveland, and their Manhattan entourage had marched across to meet the Brooklyn delegation; after the fortunate thirteen thousand who held Tiffany-engraved invitations to the opening ceremonies had gone home; after hours of official speeches, prayers, cannon shots, bells, and cheers; after fourteen tons of fireworks had exploded into dazzling streams; after an armada of beribboned boats had squeezed out of the harbor; after a beneficent moon had risen over fourteen years of toil and intrigue—anyone with a penny could cross the Brooklyn Bridge.

John Roebling (1806–1869), the virtuosic engineer (see pages 42–43), had conceived of the bridge in 1855. His descriptions make it clear that he had worked out every aspect of the bridge, from its two colossal granite towers to its four suspended steel cables, in minute detail well in advance of June 1869, when approval for the bridge was granted. On June 28, 1869, while determining the Brooklyn tower site, Roebling's foot was crushed, ironically, by a ferry. Three weeks later, before ground had been broken on the bridge that would be his elegy, Roebling died of tetanus.

The task of bringing the bridge into being was passed to Roebling's son, the fair-haired, observant, and hardworking engineer Washington. He was thirty-two years old. The epic story of how he executed his father's design has been told many times, most notably by David McCullough in his authoritative account, *The Great Bridge*. The creation of the bridge was an enormous undertaking, whether measured by its size and design innovation, the expenditure of human effort, or the political intrigue that accompanied its construction.

Washington Roebling's greatest challenge was founding the two towers over which the steel cables would be spun. For this he used giant pneumatic caissons that were sunk 45 feet (14 meters) to bedrock in Brooklyn and 78 feet (24 meters) to hard sand in Manhattan over three miserably difficult years. Directing the work in and out of the caissons, Roebling suffered an attack of caisson's disease in 1872 that left him barely able to see, walk, or write. For nine years he would oversee the construction from afar through the voice and hands of his remarkable wife, Emily. Emily meticulously transcribed her husband's directives, delivered them to the site, explained them when necessary, and stood by him as accusations, threats, and humiliations mounted in his absence. Washington, however, did what he had resolved to do. Emily was honored with the first ride over the completed bridge and did so with a rooster, a symbol of victory, in her lap.

As the quintessential American emblem, the bridge's heavy Gothic portals and ethereal web of cables have inspired generations of poets and artists. Its image has graced baseball programs, wallpaper, china, stamps, stock certificates, and more than a few biceps. For newly arrived immigrants the bridge, designed and built by immigrants, was their first inkling of the promise of America. Since its opening day, the Brooklyn Bridge has tugged on the human heart for as many reasons as there are hearts.

**Washington Augustus Roebling (1837–1926)**

**Emily Warren Roebling (1843–1903)**

The completed Manhattan anchorage, seen in a July 1876 photo, would be joined to the Brooklyn anchorage in August with the stringing of the first wire rope.

| Crossing | East River | Designer/Engineer | John A. Roebling, Washington A. Roebling | Completed | 1883 Longest suspension bridge 1883–1903 | Span | 1,595 feet/486 meters | Materials | steel, granite | Type | suspension |

Built as the centerpiece of the 1889 Exposition Universelle in Paris, the Eiffel Tower is a dizzying web of twelve thousand pieces of wrought iron, each designed independently to reflect variable inclinations and bear different loads. Eiffel's achievement at Garabit was essential to the design for his immortal tower.

Massif Central

Saint-Flour

Aurilla

GARABIT
VIADUCT

Truyère River

Gustave Eiffel's expressive mastery of metal earned him the appellation "iron magician." His metal construction firm, G. Eiffel et Compagnie, opened with Théophile Seyrig in 1868, would endure for a hundred years. By 1880, at the height of his career, Eiffel was working on projects in a dozen countries. The photograph is by Nadar, who specialized in portraits of the nineteenth-century French intelligentsia.

# Garabit Viaduct

Gustave Eiffel's (1832–1923) best known works—the armature of the Statue of Liberty, the dome of the Nice Observatory, and his ultimate creation, the tower that bears his name—are such landmarks that they overshadow his considerable international achievements as a bridge builder. The hundreds of bridges—portable bridges, military bridges, railway bridges, and footbridges—Eiffel would build and perfect over a lifetime were a prelude to his last and most significant bridge, the Garabit Viaduct.

"This is therefore a double success for me, first for my pride and second for the importance of the work which is exactly the type to put me among the companies to be reckoned with," wrote a proud Eiffel to his mother in 1867 upon winning his first big contract to build two viaducts at Neuvial and Rouzat. He went on to build a number of high-piered railway viaducts to service the rapidly expanding mining industry in the iron-rich, though topographically inhospitable, Massif Central region in the south of France.

Eiffel's challenge at Garabit was not only to cross the deep valley over the Truyère River but to create a structure that could withstand, despite its great height, the high winds that swept through the Massif Central's steep gorges. Having set up meteorological stations throughout France to collect data on aerodynamic forces, Eiffel had vast empirical knowledge of wind action.

At Garabit, Eiffel proposed a parabolic-arched viaduct similar to the Maria-Pia Viaduct (1877), which he had built over the Douro River in Oporto, Portugal. The recent availability of cheap steel (by the 1870s its price had fallen 75 percent) made feasible the long spans of both viaducts. As at Douro, the bridge crosses the ravine in five spans. The two short spans on either side of the valley are supported by metal piers on masonry bases shaped like truncated pyramids; the tallest of these piers is 294 feet (90 meters). The 540-foot (165-meter) central span was supported by an arch shaped like a crescent moon. Each half of the arch was suspended by steel cables from the deck while its components were fastened together and built out to midspan. Standing 400 feet (122 meters) above water, the viaduct was for many years the tallest bridge in the world.

Aerodynamics continued to engage Eiffel's brilliant, persistent mind. Five years later the lessons learned at Garabit would inspire the Eiffel Tower. In 1912 he built the first aerodynamic laboratory in France, where he continued to work until his death in 1923.

The Maria-Pia Viaduct has a 525-foot (160-meter) central span. On the basis of its acclaimed design, Eiffel would win the Garabit contract.

*The railroad viaducts that Eiffel designed…between 1869 and 1884 exemplify a method and an aesthetic that found their ultimate celebration in the design of the Eiffel Tower.*
—Kenneth Frampton, Modern Architecture: A Critical History, 1980

| Crossing | Truyère River | Designer/Engineer | Gustave Eiffel | Completed | 1884 | Span | 540 feet/164 meters | Materials | steel | Type | arched viaduct |

Baker arranged a living model of a cantilever bridge to assuage concerns that the bridge would remain standing. In homage to the cantilever's ancient Asian origins, Baker placed Kaichi Wantanabe, his Japanese assistant, in the center.

*The [Forth Bridge] has often been criticized as being overbuilt; but this is not so. It is simply the very essence of strength.*
—David Plowden, Bridges: The Spans of North America, 1974

Forth Bridge, Queensferry, Scotland

Scotland

Dundee

**FORTH RAIL BRIDGE**

Queensferry

# Forth Bridge

One of the great monuments of the Victorian age, the Forth Railway Bridge over the Firth of Forth in Scotland, was the first large span bridge to be built entirely of steel. When it was completed, the Forth Bridge shattered all records for length, height, and the sheer volume of materials used. It remains the second-longest cantilever ever built.

The bridge was the masterpiece of Sir Benjamin Baker (1840–1907) and Sir John Fowler (1817–1898). Like James Buchanan Eads, Baker would build many types of structures but only one bridge, and it would be his magnum opus. Highlights of his varied career include the design, with Fowler, of London's first underground railways, construction of a ship to transport the obelisk Cleopatra's Needle from Egypt to London, and the damming of the Nile at Aswan.

Baker was not the first to attempt bridging the Firth of Forth, which lay critically in the path of the rail route from Edinburgh to Dundee. Thomas Bouch was commissioned to build two bridges across the firths of Forth and Tay. The first bridge to go up was the Tay; in 1879, a year after the bridge was built and Bouch was knighted for his efforts, the bridge collapsed in a gale while a train was crossing, killing more than seventy people (see pages 44–45). Bouch's career was ruined and, not surprisingly, his design for the Forth crossing was dropped.

Determined not to repeat the engineering mistakes that led to the Tay catastrophe, Baker and Fowler designed the bridge to withstand wind pressure of fifty-six pounds per foot, nearly five times the resistance of the Tay. They decided to use steel, newly legal in Britain as a building material, for its superior strength in an ancient cantilever design. In 1887 Baker published a series of articles, "Long-Span Railway Bridges," in the British journal *Engineering*, and had concluded that cantilevers were the most efficient design for long spans.

In cantilever bridges, a rigid beam projects from a base, much like a branch from a tree trunk, to support a central span. The small island of Inchgarvie in the middle of the Forth was used as a foundation for one of the bridge's three massive cantilevers; two other piers were built on the Fife and Queensferry sides. The cantilevers are connected by two suspended girder spans of 350 feet (107 meters) each, which were built out, bay by bay, at the site. Much ado was made of the design among the general public: its safety, its cost (at that time an extraordinary $15 million), and above all, its appearance (Victorian tastemaker William Morris deemed it the "supremest specimen of all ugliness").

Standing at Baker's side as the Prince of Wales declared the bridge open in 1890 was Gustave Eiffel, who had completed his landmark Parisian tower the year before. Like the Eiffel Tower, the Forth Bridge is pure structure —having no unnecessary parts—and endures as both a work of art and an icon of man's mastery over the power of the wind.

In this 1888 construction photo, an elaborate, visually dense configuration of ties and struts braces the giant tubes, 12 feet (3.66 meters) in diameter, that rise 342 feet (104 meters) from the circular caissons at the water line.

| | | | | |
|---|---|---|---|---|
| **Crossing** Firth of Forth | **Designer/Engineer** Benjamin Baker, John Fowler | **Completed** 1890<br>Longest steel cantilever in the world 1890–1917 | **Span** 1,710 feet/521 meters | **Materials** steel | **Type** cantilever truss |

# Covered Bridges

*We crossed this river by a wooden bridge, roofed and covered in on all sides, and nearly a mile in length. It was profoundly dark; perplexed, with great beams crossing and recrossing it at every possible angle; and through the broad chinks and crevices of the floor the rapid river gleamed, far down below, like a legion of eyes.*

—Charles Dickens, on crossing the Susquehanna River, 1842

It is little wonder that covered bridges have been called "kissing bridges" and "tunnels of love." They are often set in bucolic landscapes and have an aura of seclusion about them. Yet the original reason for building these romantic structures was purely practical. A burgeoning young America desperately needed ways to ford her many rivers and streams; goods had to be traded, mail carried, political aspirations forged.

Some had hoped the federal government would undertake such "internal improvements" as bridge building, but Washington was too green for that. So the task fell to an eclectic group of entrepreneurs who took timber and one basic design element—the triangular-shaped truss—and changed the look of American bridges for the next hundred years.

Why were covered bridges covered? Not, as one myth had it, so a traveler wouldn't know what kind of village awaited him until it was too late! The real reason for their romantic look speaks to Yankee practicality: the wooden supports of the bridges lasted longer when protected from the elements.

Beautiful in themselves, the intricate truss patterns that emerged in the early nineteenth century solved a practical engineering problem: how to build bridges that could span rivers without blocking the channels below.

The patterns were named for the clever men who designed them, including Theodore Burr, William Howe, and Colonel Stephen H. Long. For the most part, these early designers were not professional architects but Renaissance-type gentlemen whose engineering ability was just one of their many skills.

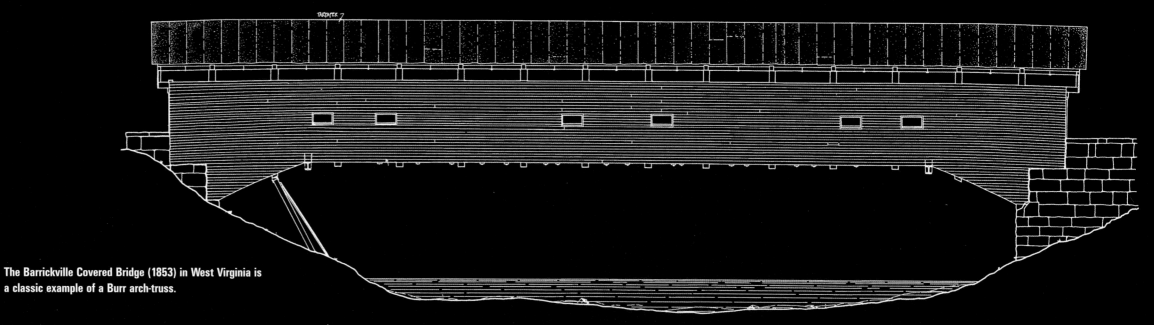

The Barrickville Covered Bridge (1853) in West Virginia is a classic example of a Burr arch-truss.

In true American fashion, those who built this country's covered bridges viewed the enterprise as a way to make a buck. Public companies were formed, shares sold. Investors planned to recoup their money through bridge tolls, even if those tolls were minuscule by today's standards: one cent for foot passengers, five cents for a one-horse sleigh, and two cents for "neat creatures." Believe it or not, "neat creatures" refers to cows.

They were men like the red-haired, long-nosed Ithiel Town of Connecticut, who patented his popular "lattice truss" covered-bridge design in 1820. Town subsequently charged builders $1.00 per foot for using it with his permission, $2.00 without. Thanks to patent agents who aggressively hawked his design throughout the countryside, hundreds of Town lattice bridges were built in New England in the nineteenth century.

It is estimated that more than ten thousand covered bridges were built in the United States from 1805 until 1885. But many of these bridges came down almost as quickly as they went up, their wooden frames vulnerable to fires, floods, and natural disasters. Why, then, were they made from timber rather than the more durable stone? Because bridge builders looked around them and saw virgin forests as far as the eye could see. Lumber was plentiful, cheap and, in some cases, free.

In the twentieth century, as the car replaced the horse and buggy and superhighways began crisscrossing the landscape, covered bridges began to disappear at an alarming rate. By 1954 there were less than two thousand left.

But just in time, preservationists and others recognized their charm. Now the remaining covered bridges are not only a living piece of history but also valuable tourist attractions for their towns. Celebrated in prose, poetry, and song, covered bridges represent a more innocent age when boys and girls swung from bridge rafters on summer days and placards inside the bridges advertised such popular remedies as Kikapoo Indian Oil, a "blood, stomach, kidney and liver regulator."

Yes, some were used for smooching. One bridge was actually called the Kissing Bridge, but it's long gone. It crossed De Voor's Mill Stream in New York City at what is now the intersection of Second Avenue and 52nd Street.

Covered bridge in Rockland, Delaware, c. 1920.

Humpback Covered Bridge, Dunlaps Creek, Virginia, 1857.

*. . . asked to build an epoch-making suspension bridge that shall be drawbridge as well, [the Londoner] builds — in the nineteenth century — something like a medieval castle of granite, makes its towers look like a cross between a pair of Baptist chapels and Rhineland fortresses, spreads it massively across sky and water, and, at the peak point of London's power and modernity, he creates a bridge suitable for King Arthur…in order, one supposes, to disguise from himself the fact that he has really built a masterpiece of engineering.*

—V.S. Pritchett, London Perceived, 1962

The bridge, shown here under construction in 1889, was technically advanced. Rather than installing hand-operated winches to raise and lower the bascules, as had been the case with other bascule bridges, Barry designed a hydraulic system, powered by steam engines, to be concealed in the towers, and executed this system in duplicate to minimize the risk of failure.

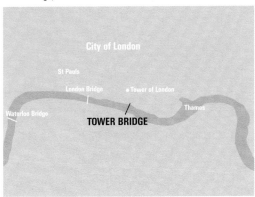

City of London

St Pauls

London Bridge

Tower of London

Waterloo Bridge

Thames

**TOWER BRIDGE**

# Tower Bridge

By the end of the nineteenth century, the eastward growth of the city of London was so great that London Bridge could no longer bear the heavy congestion its central location imposed on it. So it was with great anticipation that Londoners awaited the completion of the Tower Bridge, a downriver Thames crossing, designed by Sir Horace Jones and engineered by Sir John Wolfe-Barry.

Construction began in 1886. Once the bridge was completed in 1894, however, a shock of horror flashed through the city. Critics were appalled by the deviation of the finished bridge from the plans that had been exhibited before the cornerstone was laid. Jones's original plans had been simple yet impressive, adhering to a medieval style that was favored at the time. But Jones died in 1887, allowing Barry to take greater artistic license than he could have under the designer's supervision.

The June 30, 1894, issue of *The Builder* blasted the bridge as "the most monstrous and preposterous architectural sham that we have ever known" and refused to "waste plates" in the magazine by printing a photograph of it. To give Jones his due, he had designed the towers to harmonize architecturally with the looming medieval Tower of London nearby.

The final bridge was engineered very soundly, saving Barry's reputation. The Tower Bridge is the only movable bridge of the twenty-nine bridges on the Thames. Each bascule—the two pieces of the roadway that meet in the middle of the span and are raised and lowered in a mere minute and a half to allow ships to pass under—weighs over 1,000 tons (907 tonnes). The bascules, once raised and lowered more than a dozen times a day, are not opened much anymore because of decreased boat traffic, although occasionally sightseers are treated to a ceremonial raising of the roadway.

Popular sentiment has become much more positive over the years, and Tower Bridge is now one of London's best loved and most recognizable landmarks. Even architectural critic Eric de Maré, one of the bridge's most outspoken critics, writes that the British "have grown fond of the old fraud… and we must admit that it has carried on its task with admirable regularity and efficiency."

The bridge towers are of steel-frame construction and covered with extremely ornate, exuberantly Victorian masonry of Cornish granite and Portland stone. They are 206 feet (63 meters) high, and are linked at the 140-foot (43-meter) mark by two steel walkways that were closed to the public in 1909, when the government mounted anti-aircraft cannons on these precariously light footways; they were reopened in 1982.

| Crossing | Thames River | Designer/Engineer | Sir Horace Jones, Sir John Wolfe-Barry | Completed | 1894 | Central span | 200 feet/61 meters | Materials | masonry, steel | Type | Bascule |

*The confrontation of rail and city posed one of the major technical and aesthetic puzzles of the Industrial Revolution....[The] Hell Gate Bridge... symbolized the era with all its pretension, ambiguity, and power.*
—David P. Billington, The Tower and The Bridge, 1983

The Smithfield Street Bridge (1882) in Pittsburgh was Lindenthal's first major bridge commission. A lenticular, or lens-shaped, truss, the bridge was a harbinger of the diverse bridges that would emanate from Lindenthal's devoted exploration of steel structure.

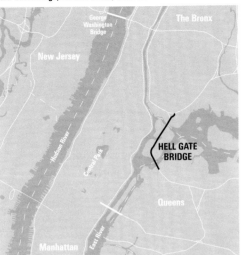

# Hell Gate Bridge

The bridge is named after the Hell Gate, the name given by Dutch sailors to the narrow, dangerous channel between Astoria, Queens, and Ward's Island.

When completed in 1916, Gustav Lindenthal's Hell Gate Bridge was the longest steel arch in the world. It was also the most visible component of the New York extension of the Pennsylvania Railroad, a vast and costly scheme that finally connected the line to New England. Today, however, it is the least known of New York City's eight major bridges.

Gustav Lindenthal (1850–1935), a giant in bridge history, was born in Moravia and emigrated to the United States in 1874. By the time he was thirty, he had his own engineering practice in Pittsburgh. Apparently self-taught, Lindenthal was soon recognized for what Tom Buckley in a 1991 *New Yorker* article described as "the extraordinary intelligence, energy, and self-discipline that enabled him to teach himself mathematics, engineering theory, metallurgy, hydraulics, estimating, management, and everything else a successful bridge designer had to know— not to mention, in his case, English." His ambition soon brought him to New York, where he oversaw the completion of the Williamsburg Bridge (1903), redesign of the Manhattan Bridge (1909), and design of the Queensboro Bridge (1909).

The Hell Gate Bridge is the chief element of a rail link that consists of two additional bridges (the Little Hell Gate Bridge, a truss, and the Bronx Kill Bridge, a bascule) and a series of viaducts and overpasses that stretch an unprecedented 3.2 miles (5.1 kilometers) from Queens to the Bronx. Lindenthal considered two arch designs: the first, inspired by Eiffel's Garabit Viaduct, was crescent-shaped; the second was a flatter, spandrel arch. Preferring massive forms that looked strong and were, Lindenthal selected the latter. He decided the bridge would appear even more stable if he increased the distance between the upper and lower chords of the arch and situated it between two massive masonry towers (which were not structurally necessary). The merits of the recurved arch and the towers have been discussed at length by critics. What is not debated is the four-track bridge's strength: its arch sustains a compressive force of a hundred and fifty thousand tons, requiring the heaviest girders ever fabricated.

The elegant, 100-foot (30-meter)-high viaduct piers were made of concrete instead of the crisscrossed steel girders first proposed because city officials feared that inmates of the Ward's Island psychiatric hospital and Randall's Island correctional institution would climb them and escape.

Lindenthal is remembered for the originality and boldness of his designs; for the Hell Gate Bridge, which is his masterpiece; and for mentoring two men, Othmar Ammann and David Steinman, who would eclipse him to become the most prominent bridge builders of the twentieth century.

For all his accomplishments, Lindenthal would die unfulfilled, having never built a bridge across the Hudson River, his all-consuming obsession and career leitmotif from the first time he advanced the idea in 1888 until his death. That span, the George Washington Bridge (1931; see pages 72-73), would be built by his former assistant Ammann.

Time's march is a poignant, sometimes ironic tune: the view of the Hell Gate Bridge, the last hurrah of the railway era, would be obstructed in 1936 by the completion of the nearby Triborough Bridge, another Ammann creation built to accommodate the automobile.

| Crossing East River at Hell Gate | Designer/Engineer Gustav Lindenthal | Completed 1916<br>Longest steel arch span 1916–31 | Span 977 feet/298 meters | Materials steel | Type arch |
|---|---|---|---|---|---|

Thy long, pale, floating vapor-pennants, tinged with delicate purple,
The dense and murky clouds out-belching from thy smokestack,
Thy knitted frame, thy springs and valves, the tremulous twinkle of thy wheels,
Thy trains of cars, behind, obedient, merrily following,
Through gale or calm, now swift, now slack, yet steadily careering;
Type of the modern—emblem of motion and power—pulse of the continent…
—Walt Whitman, "To a Locomotive in Winter", 1855

Darius crowded as many people as possible into his photos in order to sell them each a print for fifty cents. In this view, an 80-ton (73-tonne) Lima Shay train built in 1913 rests on a wooden trestle bridge.

# Bloedel Donovan's Bridge

The railroad revolutionized bridge building. By 1850, when the steam engine was coming into its own, and America was voraciously pursuing industrialization and the exploitation of her natural resources, a spate of new bridge technologies were developed. Because railway bridges had to bear not only massive weight but moving weight as well, the basic bridge—a beam over water—had to be strengthened by adding support piers or by undergirding the structure with an elaborate scaffolding called a truss, a structure made of elements arranged in the form of a triangle.

In sharp contrast to Europe, America possessed vast and abundant forests. Wood—plentiful, economical, and easy to shape and maintain—was the material of choice for a young nation eager to connect its expanse from end to end with bridges. Timber bridges could also last a long time— if they survived their dual enemies of fire and weather.

To provide a strong structure at minimal cost, the builders of this pile-and-beam bridge over the Sauk River ingeniously used logs above and below the ties to form the spans.

By the end of the nineteenth century, loggers in the Pacific Northwest had exhausted the forests located closest to roads and waterways. The locomotive gave access to vast new tracts of timber, which was fashioned into bridges to cross rivers and ravines, provided rail ties and energy for the trains, and made it possible to cut still deeper into the forests.

The restless energy of the logging industry was captured in a series of extraordinary photographs, three of which are shown here, taken over a period of fifty years by Darius Kinsey (1869–1945). Kinsey, loaded with a hundred pounds of camera equipment, traveled throughout the Pacific Northwest, creating a photographic record, ostensibly of locomotives, but also preserving for history the temporary wooden bridges built for them. He sent the negatives back to his wife, Tabitha (1875–1963), in Seattle for printing.

In order to reach a timber stand on the north side of the Skykomish River, Bloedel Donovan Lumber Mills constructed a wooden bridge in 1920 at a cost of $60,000. The 70-ton (64-tonne) locomotive traveling across the bridge in the large photograph is a Climax Number 11 built in 1923. In 1935, when much of the transportation of timber was being contracted to truck loggers, planks were laid down and both trains and trucks shared the bridge until the mid-1940s, when rail service ended. Wooden bridges, too, would be replaced with more substantial iron ones.

In 1940 Kinsey fell off a tree stump and, though not injured, never took another photo. He spent the last five years of his life cataloging his work; Tabitha survived him by eighteen years. Both died not knowing of their heroic contribution to photography or today's understanding of how industry transformed the landscape.

The legacy of Darius and Tabitha Kinsey, seen here in a self-portrait taken about 1906, is a body of 6,000 photographs that document the landscape and logging industry of the Pacific Northwest.

| Crossing | Skykomish River | Designer/Engineer | unknown | Completed | 1920; now destroyed | Length | unknown | Materials | wood | Type | truss |
|---|---|---|---|---|---|---|---|---|---|---|---|

*Make no little plans; they have no magic to stir men's blood... Make big plans; aim high in hope and work, remembering that a noble, logical diagram once recorded will never die, but long after we are gone will be a living thing, asserting itself with ever-growing insistency.*
—Daniel Burnham, 1907

The 1920s saw the construction of several landmark buildings on Michigan Avenue, including the ornate Wrigley Building (1924), designed by Graham, Anderson, Probst & White, seen here framed by the opened bridge leaves.

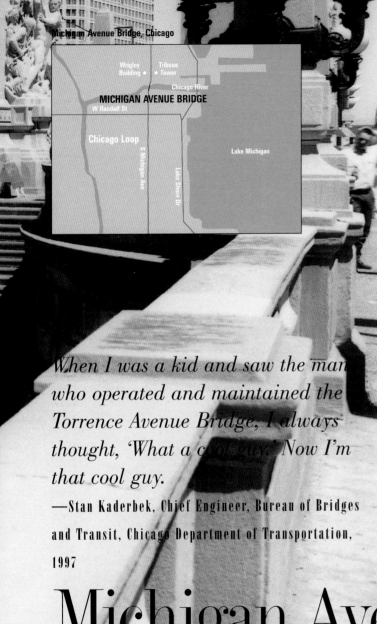

Michigan Avenue Bridge, Chicago

Wrigley Building •   • Tribune Tower

Chicago River

**MICHIGAN AVENUE BRIDGE**

W Randolf St

Chicago Loop

S Michigan Ave

Lake Shore Dr

Lake Michigan

*When I was a kid and saw the man who operated and maintained the Torrence Avenue Bridge, I always thought, 'What a cool guy.' Now I'm that cool guy.*

—Stan Kaderbek, Chief Engineer, Bureau of Bridges and Transit, Chicago Department of Transportation, 1997

# Michigan Avenue Bridge

As part of their visionary 1909 Chicago Plan, Daniel Burnham and Edward Bennett conceived of a grand connection between Grant and Lincoln parks. They hoped to ease the increasing traffic congestion downtown and, more important, distinguish Chicago architecturally with a bridge as beautiful and monumental as those of the world's great cities.

Burnham, known as "the city beautifier," had no doubt formulated his grand civic scheme for Chicago when he planned that city's influential, classically designed 1893 World Columbian Exposition. Studying Athens, Rome, Paris, and other cities, Burnham sought to mold Chicago on what he felt were the best civic designs for the benefit of the population.

The Michigan Avenue Bridge was a crucial link in marshaling Chicago's transportation pattern along the Chicago Plan guidelines. Before it was built, Michigan Avenue ended at the Chicago River and almost half of Chicago's north-south traffic squeezed through at the Rush Street swing bridge, which was also the first bridge encountered by ships entering from Lake Michigan.

After Burnham's death in 1912, Bennett took over the design of the bridge with the assistance of engineers Thomas G. Pihlfeldt and Hugh Young. The bridge was a refinement of a trunnion bascule design, a type of

movable bridge employed in Chicago almost without exception since the first one, the Cortland Street Bridge, was completed in 1902.

Bascules are drawbridges, used since medieval times. Derived from the French *bascule* ("seesaw"), a trunnion bascule works by pivoting on a horizontal shaft, the trunnion. The bridge's two leaves, each of which weighs 3,340 tons (3,030 tonnes), are raised and lowered by gears hidden in the bridge houses and powered by a 50-horsepower motor. The bridge is so finely balanced that when it is painted—nearly 2,000 pounds of paint are used—it must be recalibrated.

The Michigan Avenue Bridge was the city's masterpiece: the world's first double-leaf, double-deck trunnion bascule bridge, capable of handling two levels of traffic and clearing the channel in under sixty seconds. Over the decades, many aspects of Burnham's plan, notably the Michigan Avenue Bridge, were realized. When people think of Chicago, the image of the bridge comes first and effortlessly to mind.

**Four massive limestone bridge houses create a monumental approach. They are adorned with heroic relief sculptures by J. E. Fraser and Henry Herring.**

**The City of Chicago owns and operates thirty-seven movable bridges, more than any other city in the world; since 1902, every movable bridge with the exception of two has been of the trunnion bascule type. Indeed, the trunnion bascule is so identified with the city that it is referred to internationally as a "Chicago-type" bridge.**

| Crossing | Chicago River | Designer/Engineer | Edward H. Bennett, Thomas G. Pihlfeldt | Completed | 1920 | Span | 256 feet/78 meters | Materials | steel, limestone | Type | double-deck trunnion bascule |

*The idea that there is an independent art form of engineering structure has its origin in studies of Maillart's work.*
—David P. Billington, The Tower and the Bridge, 1983

Salginatobel Bridge, near Schiers, Switzerland

SALGINATOBEL

For the Tavanasa Bridge (1905) over the Rhine at Tavanasa, Switzerland, Maillart experimented with an open-spandrel form that anticipated the one at Salgina. The Tavanasa Bridge was destroyed by an avalanche in 1927.

# Salginatobel Bridge

The Roman genius for concrete forms would fade with their empire, not to be revived significantly until the period between 1870 and 1900, when concrete, now reinforced with metal inserts, was developed simultaneously and with great intensity in Germany, America, England, and France. Notable pioneers include Joseph Monier (1823–1906), a Parisian gardener whose reinforced–concrete flower pots would yield the patents from which the large German civil engineering firm of Wayss and Freytag would evolve in 1884; François Hennebique (1843–1921), a self-educated builder whose work led to concrete's first large-scale application in 1896; and Eugène Freyssinet (1879–1962), the inventor of prestressed concrete. The structural and aesthetic possibilities of reinforced concrete would reach their most sublime synthesis in the bridges of the great Swiss engineer Robert Maillart (1872–1940).

"Reinforced concrete does not grow like wood, it is not rolled like steel and has no joints like masonry," wrote Maillart in 1938. His words provide a succinct clue as to why his work was revolutionary: understanding that concrete was a structurally unique material, Maillart exploited its intrinsic properties in forms that were equally innovative. Between 1900 and 1940 Maillart built forty-seven bridges, all but three still standing, which are acclaimed for their beauty and invention. His masterpiece, the Salginatobel Bridge, spans a precipitous Alpine gorge with such graceful inevitability that its silhouette has become an icon of twentieth-century architecture.

Maillart's 1901 Züoz Bridge was the first to be constructed of hollow concrete boxes. Its spandrel walls, however, were solid, like those of traditional masonry arches. When the bridge developed cracks, Maillart began to investigate new forms. In his 1904 design for the Tavanasa Bridge, he removed the spandrel walls altogether, thus exposing the arch as well as its true structural function.

Like the Tavanasa, the 1930 Salginatobel Bridge is a hollow-box, three-hinged arch located in the Graubünden canton. However, as pointed out by David Billington, Maillart's biographer and an eminent structural historian, the Tavanasa design is transformed at Salginatobel: the stark white bridge appears to emerge from one side and leap across the ravine, liberated to breathtaking effect by the elimination of all those heavy stone elements— abutments, arcading, and facade—rendered structurally unnecessary by the use of reinforced concrete.

During the decade following the completion of the Salginatobel Bridge until his death, Maillart would build his most important works, the most famous of which is the curving Schwandbach Bridge at Schwarzenburg, exploring with technical and aesthetic virtuosity a limited number of fundamental forms. While he lived, his radical, imaginative designs were beyond most. Sigfried Giedion, the art historian who first brought his work to public attention in 1941, described Maillart's life as "a continuous fight against economic pressure and public dullness," and he died in 1940 without the recognition his work enjoys today. In 1947 the Museum of Modern Art in New York mounted an exhibition of his work—the first museum show ever devoted to the work of one engineer.

A closeup view of Salginatobel's dynamic underside reveals the increased width of the arch and cross wall (left).

| Crossing | Salgina Gorge | Designer/Engineer | Robert Maillart | Completed | 1930 | Span | 295 feet/90 meters | Materials | reinforced concrete | Type | arch |

*The George Washington Bridge over the Hudson is the most beautiful bridge in the world... It is blessed. It is the only seat of grace in the disordered city.... Here, finally, steel architecture seems to laugh.*
—Le Corbusier, When Cathedrals Were White, 1947

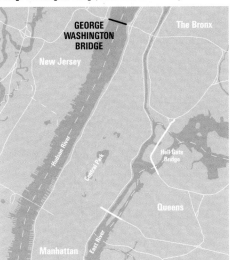

GEORGE WASHINGTON BRIDGE

New Jersey

The Bronx

Hell Gate Bridge

Queens

Manhattan

Hudson River

Central Park

East River

Othmar Hermann Ammann (1879–1965), the supremely gifted Swiss-born designer of the longest suspension spans ever built, emigrated to New York in 1904, the year he took this pensive self-portrait for his fiancée back home. As principal structural engineer under the legendary Park Commissioner Robert Moses, Ammann would reconfigure transportation patterns in the three-state area whose locus was Manhattan. He would design all six of New York's major bridges—the George Washington, Bayonne (1931), Triborough (1936), Bronx-Whitestone (1939), Throg's Neck (1961), and Verrazano Narrows (1964)—and consult on a score of North America's most significant spans.

Two years after Henry Ford introduced the first mass-produced car in 1908, 485,000 cars were registered in America. By 1929 that number skyrocketed to 26.7 million. Nowhere was vehicular congestion greater than in the booming metropolis of Manhattan, where the need for a cohesive transportation system was acute.

With the formation in 1921 of what would come to be called the Port Authority of New York and New Jersey, the Hudson crossing envisioned by many for over a century would finally be realized. Designed by Othmar H. Ammann and built during the Depression, the George Washington Bridge was described by Franklin Delano Roosevelt at its dedication in 1931 as "almost superhuman in perfection." At the time it was the world's longest suspension bridge and fundamentally changed the way long spans were designed.

Ammann's bridge, like his campaign to obtain the commission, was extremely well planned. To build it, Ammann had to navigate dense political and professional machinations, which have been chronicled in skillful detail by historians Jameson Doig and Henry Petroski.

The George Washington Bridge, locally called the GWB, succeeded technically, aesthetically, financially, and geographically. It revolutionized long-span design by eliminating the need for heavy and costly stiffening trusses, resulting in a strong bridge that was elegant and economical. Genius was also manifested in its location between West 178th Street in New York and Fort Lee, New Jersey, where the Hudson is narrowest, simplifying construction, and the ground is elevated, eliminating the need for long approaches. Traffic bound in both directions was routed away from the congestion of mid-town Manhattan. With exemplary foresight, Ammann planned for the bridge's future growth: in 1946 the original six traffic lanes were increased to eight, using an area left for that purpose; fourteen lanes became available in 1962, when a lower level, also calculated into the original design, was added.

Within six years, the title of world's longest suspended span would be claimed by the Golden Gate (see pages 82-83), to be superseded in 1957 by the Mackinac (see pages 88-89), and handed back to Ammann in 1964 with the completion of his last great bridge, the Verrazano Narrows, which remains North America's longest suspension bridge. New Yorkers, still waiting in traffic, have ample time when they are on the West Side Highway to contemplate the elemental power of the George Washington Bridge, indisputably the masterwork of a master.

Consulting architect Cass Gilbert, best known for his Woolworth Building, designed monumental granite-clad bridge towers housing restaurants and observation decks, as seen in a 1926 sketch. Economic pressures, coupled with public opinion that favored the look of the exposed lattice steelwork, led to the decision to leave the 604-foot (254-meter)-high towers unsheathed.

The GWB proved Ammann's revolutionary theory that, if properly configured, the deadweight of a suspension bridge's deck and cables would be sufficient to resist heavy wind. The bridge was so strong that when a private plane crashed on its deck in December 1965, it remained, as did the pilot, unharmed.

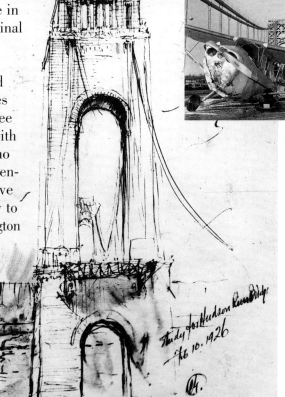

# George Washington Bridge

| Crossing | Hudson River | Designer/Engineer | Othmar H. Ammann | Completed | 1931 Longest suspended span 1931–37 | Span | 3,500 feet/1,067 meters | Materials | steel, concrete | Type | suspension |

The bridge provided hundreds of jobs during the Depression.
The cost of its construction was not paid off until 1988.

Sydney Harbor Bridge, Sydney, Australia

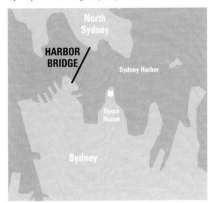

North Sydney

HARBOR BRIDGE

Sydney Harbor

Opera House

Sydney

*The Sydney is architecturally more successful than the Bayonne, incorporating as it does huge pylons nearly three hundred feet in height, which from a visual point of view as well as an engineering one, perfectly contain the arch's thrust.*

—David Plowden, Bridges: The Spans of North America, 1974

# Sydney Harbor Bridge

One of Australia's most recognizable landmarks and arguably the world's most dramatically situated bridge is the Sydney Harbor Bridge, whose distinctive arched profile inspired its affectionate nickname, "the old coat hanger." Since the day it opened in 1932, the charismatic structure has been synonymous with Sydney.

Interestingly enough, the bridge was not planned as an arch. John Job Crew Bradfield (1867–1943), chief engineer of the Public Works Department of New South Wales, had fielded numerous proposals for the bridge and had prepared one of his own. But after seeing and being very much influenced by Gustav Lindenthal's powerful Hell Gate Bridge (see pages 64-65), Bradfield scrapped his earlier cantilever design for an arch bridge. Subsequently, a two-hinged arch design by Sir Ralph Freeman (1880–1950) of the firm Dorman Long was implemented. There is some question about who originated the design; it appears that Freeman modified Bradfield's design.

Arch bridges ordinarily require falsework—elaborate scaffolding that supports the arch during construction. Because the Sydney Harbor Bridge was built over the deepest part of the harbor, the use of such temporary support was impractical. Instead, the two halves of the arch were cantilevered out from each bank until they could be joined at midspan. The deck is supported by steel cables suspended from the arch of steel girders and plates. It is an extremely strong and exceedingly wide bridge. In fact, with a deck width of 160 feet (49 meters), it is the broadest in the world. Its roadway carries four rail and tram tracks, eight traffic lanes, and pedestrian walkways.

The bridge is flanked by a pair of ornamental, Egyptoid pylons, which, until 1990, when they were adapted as ventilators for a new underground tunnel, had no functional purpose other than to provide visual reassurance of the bridge's stability. The bridge differs from its near twin, the Hell Gate Bridge, in one important respect: the arch's upper chord terminates just before the pylons, thus clarifying the true structural role of the arch's lower chord, which springs from the abutments; at Hell Gate the upper chord is buried in the masonry tower.

Ironically, the Bayonne Bridge between Newark, New Jersey, and Staten Island, New York, another immense though far lighter steel arch designed by Othmar Ammann, opened just months before the Sydney bridge. A mere 5 feet (1.5 meters) longer, the Bayonne arch would dash Sydney's claim to the title of the world's longest steel arch bridge.

Nonetheless, the *Australian Worker* praised the Sydney Harbor Bridge upon its completion, deeming it not just a bridge but a symbol "of what shall yet become universal." And immediately after its opening, the Sydney Harbor Bridge was written about, photographed, painted, reproduced on postcards, and miniaturized as souvenirs. Suddenly the world knew Sydney, and Sydney, now possessing the world's widest if not its longest bridge, began to conceive of itself on a global scale.

The city's geography is defined by the bridge. Northern Sydney is north of the bridge, southern Sydney is south. Western Sydney starts immediately west of the bridge, and the eastern suburbs are in the region to its east.

| Crossing | Sydney Harbor | Designer/Engineer | J. J. C. Bradfield, Sir Ralph Freeman | Completed | 1932 Widest long-span bridge | Span | 1650 feet/503 meters | Materials | steel | Type | arch |

# The Bridges of War

Clockwise from far left:

In an 1864 view, canvas-covered boats form a bridge made by New York engineers during the American Civil War.

The swimmers in the foreground are Japanese who built a pontoon bridge of boats across the Liuli River, China, 1937.

The body of a slain American soldier is sprawled across a narrow pontoon bridge over the Ruhr River, Germany, 1945.

Japanese soldiers carrying a pontoon bridge to a river near Yungsin, China, 1939.

A Bailey bridge over the Muemme River in Rotenburg, Germany, collapses under the weight of a 60-ton (54-tonne) tank, 1952.

A temporary bridge built by American Marine Corps engineers over a jungle stream in Guadalcanal, Solomon Islands, 1942.

A Bailey bridge under construction in England, 1944.

Military bridges are not always temporary, but many types of emergency bridges have military origins. Military bridges are of three main types: scissor-style launched bridges that are foldable and often laid by armored vehicles; floating bridges (also called pontoon or ribbon bridges); and Bailey bridges, which are built of modular panels.

Pontoon bridges utilizing a series of boats date back to the ancient Chinese, Greeks, Romans, and Persians. The most famous pontoon bridge was the two-mile span over the Hellespont (Dardanelles) constructed in 480 B.C. by Persian engineers to transport Xerxes's invading army. According to Herodotus, it was made of 676 ships stationed in two parallel rows with their keels in the direction of the current.

As the technology and mechanization of war developed, the need to move huge quantities of heavy equipment over large distances made the strategic value of bridges greater than ever. Military engineering units strove to utilize their skills to serve their own army's ability to live, move, and fight, as well as to impede the efforts—while under fire—of the opposing side's engineers. Prior to the outbreak of World War II they worked largely with primitive tools and locally available materials. In the early years of the war, crude developments included the modification of existing materials to meet short-term bridging requirements, but a new, permanent solution was required.

The military engineer's ability to influence the course of operations was soon enhanced by the development of rapid bridging equipment. The greatest achievement in this field was the invention of the Bailey bridge by Sir Donald Coleman Bailey, chief engineer at the Military Engineering Experimental Establishment at Christchurch, Dorset, England. Developed over a period of only seven months during 1941 and 1942, Bailey's simple yet highly versatile design met difficult criteria in terms of manpower requirements, transportation needs, flexibility of design, and flexibility in load-bearing capacity.

These phenomenally successful girder bridges were constructed of a series of steel lattice panels held in position by high-tensile key pins at each of the corners. The flexibility of design meant that it was possible for these girders to be multiplied, thereby providing extra length and strength as required. Although the original concept was for a simple through bridge, later developments included arches and even towers. First used operationally during the North African campaign in Tunisia during the latter part of 1942, Bailey bridges quickly became the main bridging equipment of the Allied armies.

Throughout the war these bridges were used in many configurations, from floating bridges to suspension bridges. The Bailey bridge could be altered in place, raising its load-bearing limits to accommodate heavier loads and greater volumes of traffic. They were also used in the Pacific and in China. The German "D" bridge performed similar functions.

Bailey bridges were a common site at river crossings for many years after the war. They supplemented the old bridges that were deteriorating under the strain of the increase in volume and weight of modern traffic.

*All the shrewd contrivances and safeguards of man had been thrown out of gear by thirty seconds' twitching of the earth-crust.*

—Jack London, "The Story Of An Eyewitness," Collier's, 1906

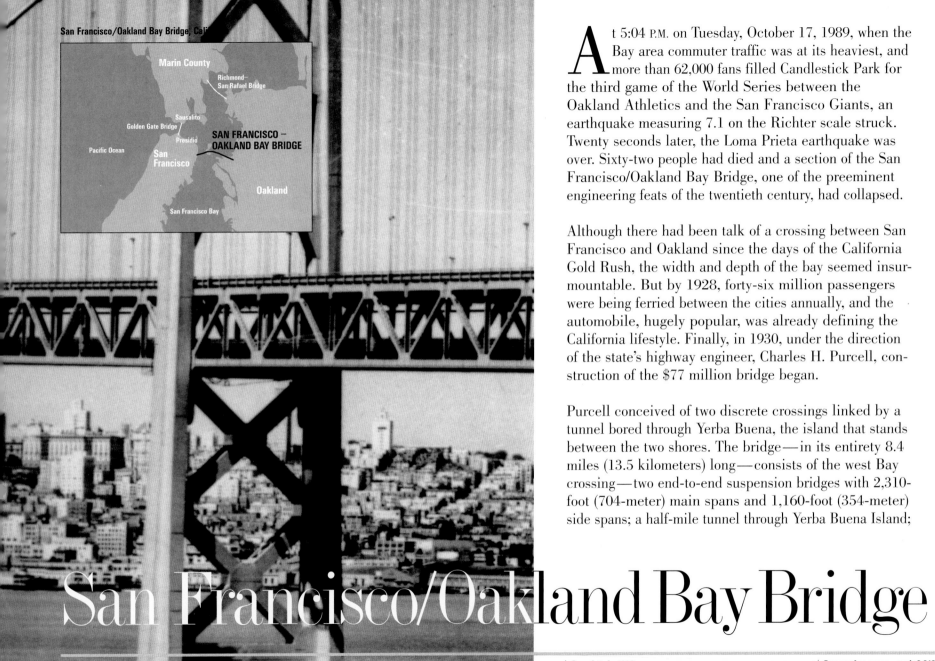

Marin County

Richmond–
San Rafael Bridge

Sausalito

Golden Gate Bridge

Presidio

Pacific Ocean

San
Francisco

**SAN FRANCISCO –
OAKLAND BAY BRIDGE**

Oakland

San Francisco Bay

# San Francisco/Oakland Bay Bridge

At 5:04 P.M. on Tuesday, October 17, 1989, when the Bay area commuter traffic was at its heaviest, and more than 62,000 fans filled Candlestick Park for the third game of the World Series between the Oakland Athletics and the San Francisco Giants, an earthquake measuring 7.1 on the Richter scale struck. Twenty seconds later, the Loma Prieta earthquake was over. Sixty-two people had died and a section of the San Francisco/Oakland Bay Bridge, one of the preeminent engineering feats of the twentieth century, had collapsed.

Although there had been talk of a crossing between San Francisco and Oakland since the days of the California Gold Rush, the width and depth of the bay seemed insurmountable. But by 1928, forty-six million passengers were being ferried between the cities annually, and the automobile, hugely popular, was already defining the California lifestyle. Finally, in 1930, under the direction of the state's highway engineer, Charles H. Purcell, construction of the $77 million bridge began.

Purcell conceived of two discrete crossings linked by a tunnel bored through Yerba Buena, the island that stands between the two shores. The bridge—in its entirety 8.4 miles (13.5 kilometers) long—consists of the west Bay crossing—two end-to-end suspension bridges with 2,310-foot (704-meter) main spans and 1,160-foot (354-meter) side spans; a half-mile tunnel through Yerba Buena Island;

the east Bay crossing—a cantilever bridge with a main span of 1,400 feet (427 meters); and a long viaduct to the Oakland shore. When finished, both crossings broke world records for their length.

The greatest challenge in constructing the west Bay crossing was the sinking of the central anchorage for its two suspension bridges to bedrock 220 feet (67 meters) below the water at low tide, a feat accomplished by the use of a multiple-dome caisson invented by Daniel Moran. The east Bay crossing, although overshadowed by the unprecedented length of the west Bay bridge, garnered its own accolades: when complete, it was the country's longest cantilever, and it still boasts the world's deepest bridge pier, which is sunk 242 feet (74 meters) below water level. Almost as soon as the bridge was opened in 1936, traffic exceeded levels predicted for 1950.

The Loma Prieta earthquake damage seriously impacted Bay area commuters, about 270,000 of whom traverse the bridge daily, so the bridge was quickly repaired. Estimates of the cost of a seismic retrofit are so high (about $1.3 billion) that the state has proposed building a new crossing for about $1.5 billion. To appease Bay area residents who are agitated about plans to change their skyline, the California Department of Transportation has created on-line bridge simulations that allow viewers to "fly through" the three new bridge designs under consideration.

When the earthquake hit, bolts holding a section of the upper deck on the truss section of the east Bay crossing were sheared off, causing a portion of the deck to unhinge and fall onto the lower deck.

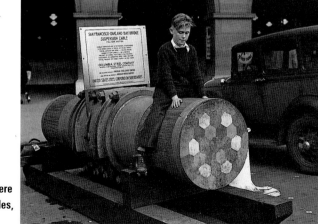

Seventy thousand miles of wire were used in the suspension bridge cables, seen here full size.

| Crossing San Francisco Bay | Designer/Engineer Charles H. Purcell | Completed 1936 | Suspension spans each 2,310 feet/704 meters | Materials steel | Type Suspension, cantilever, truss |
| --- | --- | --- | --- | --- | --- |
| | | | Cantilever span 1,400 feet/427 meters | | |

The Rogue River Bridge (1932) at Gold Beach, Oregon was the first bridge built in the United States to utilize prestressed concrete, a technique pioneered in the 1910s by French engineer Eugène Freyssinet that would revolutionize the use of concrete.

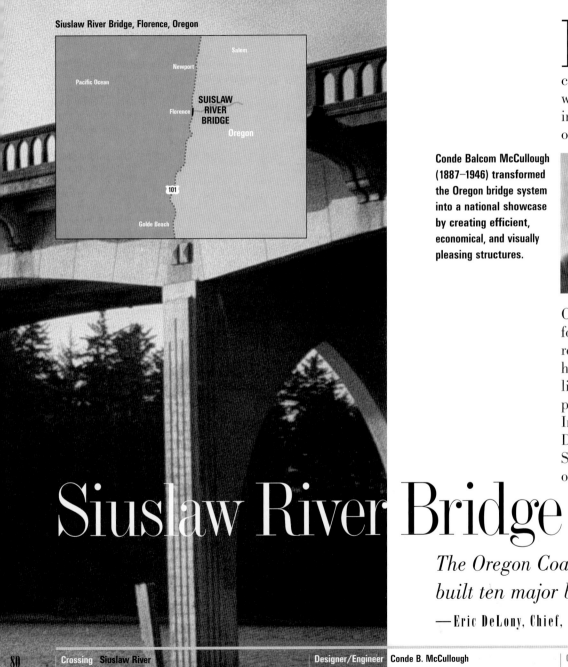

Salem

Newport

Pacific Ocean

**SUISLAW
RIVER
BRIDGE**

Florence

Oregon

101

Golde Beach

**Conde Balcom McCullough (1887–1946) transformed the Oregon bridge system into a national showcase by creating efficient, economical, and visually pleasing structures.**

R oute 101, known as the Oregon Coast Highway, is Conde B. McCullough's masterpiece. Ten major bridges of his creation, built during the 1930s, cross its route in a panoply of styles and materials that was leagues ahead of the designs of anyone else working in the United States at that time. Beyond the sheer variety of the bridge types employed, the collection of bridges was innovatively engineered. How did McCullough—born in South Dakota, educated in Iowa, and with no known trips abroad—obtain his far-reaching understanding of bridge design?

Scholars of his work attribute his breadth of knowledge to a lawsuit. After graduating from Iowa State College in 1910, McCullough worked in Des Moines for James Marsh, whose firm was experimenting with reinforced-concrete bridge design. He subsequently was hired by the Iowa State Highway Commission, which, like many state agencies, was reevaluating its highway programs in light of the increasing use of automobiles. In 1912 Marsh was sued for patent infringements by Daniel Luten, a designer of reinforced-concrete bridges. Siding with Marsh, the state put McCullough in charge of collecting evidence—600 pages of documentation,

150 exhibits, and 15 models on concrete bridge engineering from the Romans onward—that would be used to prove, by 1916, that Luten's claims were baseless. By compiling a persuasive body of evidence that would win the suit for his old employer, McCullough acquired enough in-depth knowledge about the capabilites of concrete to serve him for a lifetime.

From 1919 to 1935 McCullough was the state bridge engineer in Oregon. With funds from Franklin D. Roosevelt's Public Works Administration program, he oversaw the construction of hundreds of bridges. His ten major bridges on the Oregon Coast Highway, including the three seen here, represent McCullough's work at the pinnacle of his career.

The Siuslaw River Bridge is a good example of his eclectic structural and design vocabulary. It is a movable bridge, a double-leaf bascule that is flanked by two tied concrete arches, each 154 feet (47 meters) long. The bridge and its approaches are enhanced with detailing and ornamentation—as seen in the pylons, bridge houses, bracketed balustrades, and approach arches— that reflect McCullough's masterly use of concrete and exuberant quotation of Art Deco, Egyptian, and Gothic motifs.

**The Yaquina Bay Bridge (1936) in Newport, Oregon, is an elegant combination of steel and reinforced-concrete arches.**

# Siuslaw River Bridge

*The Oregon Coast Highway has one of the great, perhaps unequaled, collections of bridges in the United States....That Conde McCullough built ten major bridges on it, no two alike, in the space of eight years, during the height of the Depression, is nothing short of amazing.*

—Eric DeLony, Chief, Historic American Engineering Record, conversation with the author, 1997

| Crossing Siuslaw River | Designer/Engineer Conde B. McCullough | Completed 1936 | Span 140 feet/43 meters | Materials concrete, steel | Type double-leaf bascule |

*And the weather! The wind roars, the fog gets thick and soupy. When it's icy up here, it's like a skating rink 75 stories above the water. Sometimes, though, we're actually above the fog. Down below, tourists are shivering while we're up here in T-shirts getting a tan.*
—Bud Wiley, Golden Gate Bridge painter in "Above It All," Life, 1995

The devastation of a 1906 earthquake, World War I, and the Depression, coupled with political resistance and opposition from those who thought the bridge would ruin the beauty of the Bay area (here the view north toward Marin County), delayed its construction for half a century.

GOLDEN GATE BRIDGE /

Marin County

Richmond–San Rafael Bridge

Sausalito

Presidio

San Francisco–Oakland Bay Bridge

Pacific Ocean

San Francisco

Oakland

San Francisco Bay

# Golden Gate Bridge

The majestic Golden Gate Bridge, a magnet for bridge lovers the world over, is synonymous not only with the San Francisco Bay area but with large-scale suspension bridges. Today it is difficult to imagine a time when it did not exist. Before it was built, however, most thought it never would be.

There were exceptions. Joseph B. Strauss (1870–1938), a veteran bridge designer chosen as the chief engineer after competing against proposals by eleven other firms, had lobbied for two decades to have the span erected. To realize what would be the longest bridge yet built, Strauss hired several of his rivals as consultants, including O. H. Ammann, Charles Derleth, and Leon Moisseiff.

The bridge's greatest asset—its setting—was also its most formidable construction challenge. The best location for the south pier was a spot 1,100 feet (339 meters) from shore in deep, frigid ocean waters. Strauss planned to build an enclosed oval fender ring around the site of the pier, float out a huge caisson, and sink it with concrete. A temporary trestle roadway was built out to the pier to bring trucks, water pipes, and electricity to the site. Delays and expenses mounted as the trestle

was destroyed and had to be rebuilt twice. Strauss abandoned his original plan and turned the oval frame into a cofferdam that,

After twenty-two years, Joseph Strauss finally overcame, in his words, "the persistent opposition of influential vested interests." Ultimately, he completed the $27 million bridge only five months after the promised date and $1.3 million under budget. For his efforts Strauss received $1 million and a lifetime bridge pass.

Strauss insisted on rigorous safety precautions, including the first use on a major bridge project of hard hats and a safety net. The net saved the lives of nineteen men who fell; they subsequently formed the Half-Way-to-Hell Club.

filled with concrete, became the support for the piers. Construction of the graceful Art Deco towers then commenced. Steel for the project came from Pennsylvania via the Panama Canal; the cables were made by John A. Roebling & Sons of New Jersey.

On May 27, 1937, 200,000 people streamed across the new bridge. "Pedestrians Day" was reenacted on the bridge's fiftieth anniversary in 1987 as "Bridgewalk '87." In honor of the bridge's sixtieth anniversary, the Department of Highways created a web site (http://www.ggb60.com/) where surfers can take a virtual walk across the bridge. Today the Golden Gate Bridge—once an impossible dream, then a hard-won reality, now a legend—is a keystroke away.

Contrary to popular belief, the bridge is not painted from end to end every year. Painters are always at work but they are retouching areas that have corroded in the salt air. International Orange, the bridge's memorable trademark color, was chosen as the best complement to the bridge's natural setting.

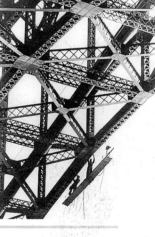

| Crossing | Golden Gate Strait | Designer/Engineer | Joseph B. Strauss | Completed | 1937 Longest bridge in the world 1937–64 | Span | 4,200 feet/1,280 meters | Materials | steel, concrete | Type | suspension |

*It was not realized that the aerodynamic forces which had proven disastrous in the past to much lighter and shorter flexible suspension bridges would affect a structure of such magnitude as the Tacoma Narrows Bridge.*
—Othmar Ammann, report to the Federal Works Agency on the Tacoma Narrows Bridge collapse, 1941

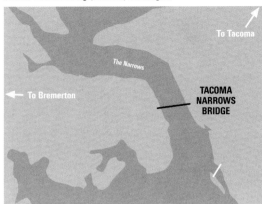

Tacoma Narrows Bridge, Tacoma, Washington

To Tacoma
The Narrows
To Bremerton
TACOMA
NARROWS
BRIDGE

Burt Farquharson, an engineering professor at the University of Washington who had been studying the bridge's movement, was there to capture the bridge's death rattle in these dramatic photographs. Here, the deck begins to twist violently from side to side.

Tons of writhing steel and concrete are ripped from the anchorages and plunge into the water.

On November 7, 1940, the Tacoma Narrows Bridge collapsed in forty-two-mile-an-hour winds that swept across Puget Sound, thirty miles south of Seattle. It had been open only four months. Even though the bridge's violent demise was documented in dramatic photographs and film footage, technical experts still disagree on the exact nature of the phenomenon that led to its landmark collapse.

When it opened, the bridge's deck undulated so much—harmlessly, it was thought—that thrill seekers sought it out to experience the rollercoasterlike ride across. Others went miles out of their way to avoid "Galloping Gertie," as the bridge was nicknamed.

Leon Moisseiff (1872–1943), a veteran designer and consultant on nearly every large suspension bridge built in America before 1940, had designed the Tacoma Narrows span with a roadway that, at thirty-nine feet (12 meters), was exceptionally narrow. The length of the center span—the third-longest suspension span in the world—was necessitated by the Narrows' swift current and poor riverbed, which prevented intermediate foundations. Supported by shallow plate girders instead of traditional deep, stiffening trusses, the proposed bridge was economical and elegant. By the 1930s, as cars replaced heavier railroad loads, the use of strengthening trusses

was becoming obsolete. Later it was realized that the sheer weight of these trusses cancelled out the effect of aerodynamic forces on the structure.

Moisseiff's enormous reputation, coupled with the recent completion of several similarly slender suspension spans, blinded bridge engineers who considered aerodynamic failure a remote possibility. The lone dissenter to the proposed design—T. L. Condron, a septuagenarian advisory engineer who recommended widening the deck—went unheeded.

Gertie came to an abrupt end. Simply put, the deck's plate girders caught the wind, rather than allowing it to pass through as it would have if there had been an open truss. This, combined with its slim proportions, made the bridge especially vulnerable. The bridge's oscillation amplified until its convolutions tore several suspenders loose, and the span broke up. Miraculously, the only fatality was a dog, Tubby, that did not manage to escape his master's car before it fell into the Narrows.

The Federal Works Agency immediately established a commission to investigate the collapse. The commission, which included Othmar Ammann and Theodore von Kármán, exonerated Moisseiff, observing that while the bridge's shortcomings were obvious in hindsight, its design had met all criteria for acceptable practice. The report's tone suggests that the engineering industry as a whole, in its relentless pursuit of streamlined bridges of unprecedented length, was guilty of ignoring aerodynamic forces in their calculations. For the next quarter century no suspension bridges would be built without a stiffening truss.

In 1992 Gertie's sunken remains were placed on the National Register of Historic Places to protect them from salvagers.

# Tacoma Narrows Bridge

| Crossing Tacoma Narrows | Designer/Engineer Leon Moisseiff | Completed 1940 Collapsed 1940 | Span 2,800 feet/854 meters | Materials steel, concrete | Type suspension |

*We were across the Rhine, on a permanent bridge; the traditional defensive barrier to the heart of Germany was pierced. The final defeat of the enemy... was suddenly, now, just around the corner.*
—General Dwight D. Eisenhower, Crusade in Europe, 1948

Twenty-eight Allied soldiers who were repairing the bridge at the time it collapsed died.

# Ludendorff Bridge

Gaping holes in the bridge deck had to be covered so Allied troops and tanks could cross.

The Ludendorff Bridge at Remagen no longer survives in a physical sense but lives on as a powerful memory of the cataclysm of World War II. A leitmotif of the last days of that war, the bridge provides insight into the altering power that fortuity can yield in dictating and, as in this case, hastening the course of history.

Built during World War I, the bridge was one of many constructed across the Rhine to facilitate the transport of German troops and materiel from east to west. One of the chief lobbyists for construction of the Rhine bridges was General Erich Ludendorff, Germany's wartime commander at the time, after whom the bridge was named.

The firm of Grün and Bilfinger designed the double-track railroad bridge as a steel arch with through-truss side spans. At each end were two fortresslike stone towers with openings for guns and interior storage space for military supplies and personnel. Trains passed over the bridge and then through a 1,200-foot (366-meter) rail tunnel bored into the Erpeler Ley, a 600-foot (183-meter) basalt cliff opposite Remagen.

With the outbreak of World War II, the bridge at Remagen became a strategic military link between Germany and the two fronts, facilitating military transport westward. Coexisting with the bridge's offensive utility was a defensive plan to demolish the bridge to prevent it from falling into enemy hands. To that end, the bridge was mined with explosives in 1938, a year before the war began. The infallibility of the contingency plan for the bridge was a given, confirmed by systematic testing of the detonator's electronic ignition system.

That the bridge would be blown up was fully anticipated by the Allied forces as well. The idea that a Rhine bridge could be seized intact was considered preposterous. Operating from this presumption, Allied troops began massive bombing of the Rhine bridges in September 1944 to disrupt Germany's communications and trap German troops on the western side of the Rhine.

On March 7, 1945, with Allied forces fast approaching, German commanders gave the order to detonate. Nothing happened. The impossible had occurred: the ignition system malfunctioned. A reluctant volunteer ran out to the bridge and lit the fuse by hand. Instead of destroying the bridge, however, the partial explosion momentarily lifted it off its foundations and returned it, albeit somewhat tenuously, to its prior position. The 9th Armored Division, the first Allied troops on the scene, scrambled across and cut wires leading to other demolition charges. Within a week, four German officers held responsible for the loss of the bridge were court-martialed and executed.

The capture of the Ludendorff Bridge significantly hastened the end of the war. Allied forces crossed what had been a formidable barrier and penetrated Germany with unanticipated speed. Indeed, in the days immediately following, 25,000 troops crossed the Rhine at Remagen and established the first Allied bridgehead in the German heartland.

For ten days almost to the minute, the bridge at Remagen was kept open, having miraculously survived attempts on both sides to blow it up. Despite round-the-clock repairs, the German demolition charges and constant Allied shelling finally took its toll. On March 17, 1945, the bridge collapsed and slowly descended into the Rhine.

Frightened German townspeople, soldiers, and officers huddled in the Erpeler Ley rail tunnel, where the detonation order was given.

| Crossing | Rhine River | Designer/Engineer | Grün and Bilfinger | Completed | 1918 | Length | 1,069 feet/326 meters | Materials | steel | Type | arch |
|---|---|---|---|---|---|---|---|---|---|---|---|
| | | | | Destroyed | 1945 | | | | | | |

David Barnard Steinman (1886–1960) grew up in a poor neighborhood under the Brooklyn Bridge, a lifelong inspiration. As an assistant to Gustav Lindenthal, he worked on the Hell Gate Bridge in New York (1916; see pages 64–65). With longtime partner Holton D. Robinson, he constructed his first major bridge, the Florianópolis Bridge in Brazil (1926), which was followed by the design of more than four hundred bridges, including the Carquinez Straits Bridge in California (1927), Mount Hope Bridge in Rhode Island (1929), St. Johns Bridge in Oregon (1931), Henry Hudson Bridge in New York (1936), and the Mackinac Bridge. The controversial Steinman was a tireless self-promoter, scholar, and prolific author and poet, whose extensive studies of aerodynamic stability expanded the possibilities of long-span suspension design.

*The Mackinac Bridge is my crowning achievement—the consummation*

—David B. Steinman, *Miracle Bridge at Mackinac*, 1957

# Mackinac Bridge

*of a lifetime dedicated to my chosen profession of bridge building.*

The onset of World War II curtailed large-scale bridge construction through the 1940s. Moreover, the 1940 collapse of the Tacoma Narrows Bridge (see pages 84–85) had a sobering, long-lasting effect on bridge design, the most visible and immediate change in which was the inclusion of deep web-truss stiffeners on every suspension bridge built thereafter. David B. Steinman's research into aerodynamic stability, in particular, would renew public and professional confidence in the viability of large-scale suspension bridges. The end of the war saw the renewal of bridge construction on both sides of the Atlantic. In Germany, an astounding 1,500 bombed-out bridges were replaced, many with cable-stayed designs that could be erected on what remained of the old bridges.

Even before 1888, when Cornelius Vanderbilt declared from the steps of the Grand Hotel on Mackinac Island, "What we need is a bridge across the Straits," there had been talk of a bridge to cross the frigid, 5-mile (8-km)-wide Straits of Mackinac (pronounced MAKinaw). But it wasn't until 1951, when reports of salt caverns under the Straits proved untrue, steel became available once again after the Korean War, and three consulting engineers—David Steinman, Othmar Ammann, and Glenn Woodruff—were selected, that plans for the bridge proceeded.

In the mid-twentieth century, all the major suspension bridges in United States were built by one of two highly skilled rivals, Othmar Ammann and David Steinman. Steinman built a great number of bridges, but Ammann was building the world's longest suspension spans. For Steinman, the Mackinac project presented a long-awaited opportunity (in fact his last) to build a bridge longer than any other. In 1953 he agreed to take the job on speculation; Ammann withdrew. To finance the bridge, $100 million worth of bonds were sold that were not paid off until July 1986.

Ground was broken on Mighty Mac in 1954. Its two steel towers rose 552 feet (168 meters) above the straits on piers that descended to a depth of 210 feet (64 meters) below water. The Mackinac Bridge, like many of Steinman's bridges, is distinguished by its color: the towers were painted ivory and the spans and cables green to express, according to Steinman, the opposite forces of tension and compression. The bridge was braced with 38-foot (12-meter) trusses; widely spaced, the deck can swing out as much as 20 feet (6 meters) on a windy day. With a critical wind velocity of infinity, it had an aerodynamic stability never before attained in a bridge. With an anchorage-to-anchorage length of 8,614 feet (2,625 meters) and a total length of nearly five miles, it was the world's longest over-all suspension bridge span for many years.

An aerial view of the catwalk suspended from the towers before the cable spinning begins gives some idea of the bridge's gargantuan proportions. Its size has inspired a number of apocryphal stories as well as the Timid Driver program to escort frightened motorists over the bridge.

| Crossing | Straits of Mackinac | Designer/Engineer | David B. Steinman | Completed | 1957 | Span | 3,800 feet/1,159 meters | Materials | steel, concrete | Type | suspension |
| --- | --- | --- | --- | --- | --- | --- | --- | --- | --- | --- | --- |
| | | | | Longest suspended span | 1957–98 | | | | | | |

*It is a work of transcendental economic importance.*
—Venezuelan President Rómulo Betancourt at the inauguration of the Lake Maracaibo Bridge, August 24, 1962

Lake Maracaibo Bridge, Maracaibo, Venezuela

Seeing the picturesque houses on stilts over Lake Maracaibo, the fourteenth-century colonizer Alonso de Ojeda was reminded of Venice, and named the place accordingly: Venezuela. Today thousands of lanky oil derricks stand in the lake, as they have since 1914, when oil was discovered there. The discovery transformed Venezuela's economy—today Venezuela is one of OPEC's largest producers—and led in the 1950s to the development of large-scale public works targeted at the country's infrastructure.

One such project, the Lake Maracaibo Bridge, also known as the Puente General Rafael Urdaneta after the Maracaibo-born hero of the country's struggle for independence from Spain, was completed in 1962. The heroic bridge, considered one of the most significant engineering achievements of the twentieth century, stretches nearly five and a half miles across Lake Maracaibo's narrow northern neck to form the first direct surface link between Maracaibo and the rest of Venezuela.

Eleven of the twelve proposals submitted in response to the Venezuelan government's request for international tenders for a bridge across the vast lake were designs in structural steel. The exception was the prestressed reinforced concrete cable-stayed design by the brilliant Italian engineer and teacher Riccardo Morandi

(1902–1989). With his peers Pier Luigi Nervi, Robert Maillart, and Félix Candela, Morandi transformed reinforced concrete from a purely structural medium to an instrument of architectural expression. The powerful, square-shouldered profile that Morandi developed at Lake Maracaibo would prove a signature design, one that he would vary in his future bridges, notably in Italy and Libya.

Morandi's design was chosen for economic and political reasons as well as for aesthetic considerations. Less expensive than steel, concrete would require less maintenance in the tropical, corrosion-producing environment. Moreover, Venezuelan workers would benefit from the experience of working in prestressed concrete, a plus for a country that was rapidly expanding in the wake of the 1958 overthrow of its military dictatorship.

The bridge consists of a total of 135 spans that gradually rise along an eastern viaduct to meet five central cable-stayed spans and then descend to the western shore. The A-shaped concrete pylons of the five central navigation spans are 303 feet (92 meters) tall. Each central span is 771 feet (235 meters) long and provides a 150-foot (46-meter) clearance for ships and tankers. To reduce costs, the design employed standardized units whenever possible. Concrete for the central superstructure was prepared in a floating mixing plant, carried up the bridge, and poured into formwork.

In early cable-stayed designs, a small number of massive cable stays were used to support the roadway and required large anchorages and deep decks. The original cables used at Maracaibo, like most used in early cable-stayed bridges, consisted of zinc-coated strands, the advantages of which included ease in handling and relatively low cost. In Lake Maracaibo's humid equatorial climate, however, they corroded and were replaced in 1980 after eighteen years of service; they now require a second refitting.

The super tanker Esso Maracaibo, shown here crossing under the bridge in 1961, rammed into the bridge in April 1964, knocking loose a 1,500-foot (457-meter) section of the bridge and claiming four lives.

As they approach the central section of the bridge, the side spans become taller and wider, and the piers change from a V shape to the pinched H shape seen here.

# Lake Maracaibo Bridge

| Crossing | Lake Maracaibo | Designer/Engineer | Riccardo Morandi | Completed | 1962 | Length | 5.4 miles/8.8 km | Materials | prestressed reinforced concrete, steel | Type | cable-stayed |

Moviemakers have long capitalized on the chameleonlike ability of a bridge to evoke danger, nostalgia, or romance. As an image, a bridge can deliver a powerful, emotional message that can be manipulated to stir up feelings of fear, honor, accomplishment, and futility.

War movies that feature bridges are a genre in themselves, often with the bridge in question taking a leading role. The best of them include: *A Bridge Too Far*, an all-star reenactment of the Allied assault in 1944 on a strategically important bridge at Arnheim, Holland; David Lean's epic *The Bridge on the River Kwai*, in which a British prisoner-of-war becomes obsessed with building a perfect railway bridge even though it will be used by the enemy to transport munitions; *For Whom the Bell Tolls*, another high-risk assignment to blow up a bridge, this time via Hemingway during the Spanish Civil War; *The Bridges at Toko-Ri*, set during the Korean War, an examination of a fighter pilot's ambivalence about war and his fear of having to bomb a set of highly defended bridges; and *The Bridge at Remagen*, a World War II story of a war-weary American unit that is ordered to capture the last bridge left standing across the Rhine before German defenders can destroy it.

Love stories, too, are set on bridges. In this genre the bridge is used as a symbol of the passage of time and as a metaphor for yearning, whether for a long lost love (*Waterloo Bridge*) or love at long last (*The Bridges of Madison County*). Morals and other matters of the heart are explored in *The Bridge of San Luis Rey*, a film that flashes back on the lives of five people killed in a bridge collapse in eighteenth-century Peru.

As a transition device, bridges are ideal. In *It's a Wonderful Life*, James Stewart plays George Bailey, the well-loved, eternally broke citizen of Bedford Falls who is about to jump off a bridge at Christmas, only to be turned around by his guardian angel, Clarence. Johnny Weismuller, in the title role in *Tarzan's New York Adventure*, makes his escape by executing a swan dive off the Brooklyn Bridge.

The Bridge of San Luis Rey, 1944

On the Town, 1949

In our everyday lives most of us drive over bridges without a second thought, but the moment a bridge appears on the big screen, it's time to clutch the popcorn boxes—something big is about to happen. Thrilling moments on bridges can be experienced in *The Wild Bunch* and *Terminator 2:Judgment Day*.

A seemingly fragile bridge can make a scene humorous; a strong one can render attempts to destroy it ridiculous. In *Swiss Miss*, Stan Laurel and Oliver Hardy become trapped on a rickety rope bridge high above an Alpine gorge, where they are met halfway by a gorilla, while a giant octopus tries to tear down the Golden Gate Bridge in *It Came from Beneath the Sea*.

Urban icons such as the Golden Gate Bridge and Brooklyn Bridge are so identified with their cities that directors routinely use them as visual shorthand to establish a movie's location in San Francisco or New York. Ditto the bridges of Paris, Pittsburgh, and St. Petersburg.

# Bridges in the Movies

The Bridge on the River Kwai, 1957

A Bridge Too Far, 1977

The Bridges of Madison County, 1995

What follows is a list of films that feature bridges in a memorable manner.

*Les Amants du Pont-Neuf* (1991)
*Bataan* (1943)
*Bitka na Neretvi* (1969)
*The Boy and the Bridge* (1959)
*The Bridge at Remagen* (1969)
*The Bridge on the River Kwai* (1957)
*The Bridge of San Luis Rey* (1929, 1944)
*A Bridge Too Far* (1977)
*The Bridges at Toko-Ri* (1954)
*The Bridges of Madison County* (1995)

*The Brooklyn Bridge* (1981)
*De Brug* (1928)
*Die Brücke* (1959)
*Dincolo de pod* (1975)
*The Cassandra Crossing* (1976)
*For Whom the Bell Tolls* (1943)
*Force 10 from Navarone* (1978)
*The Forth Road Bridge* (1965)
*The Ghost and the Darkness* (1996)
*Gunga Din* (1939)
*If Lucy Fell* (1996)
*It Came from Beneath the Sea* (1955)

*It's a Wonderful Life* (1946)
*Keeper of the Flame* (1942)
*Kogda razvodyat mosty* (1962)
*Last Platoon* (1988)
*Die Letzte Brücke* (1954)
*The Man Who Would Be King* (1975)
*Man's Hope* (1945)
*The Mountain Road* (1960)
*The Naked City* (1948)
*Nihonbashi* (1956)
*Occurrence at Owl Creek Bridge* (1962)

*Ode to Billy Joe* (1976)
*Ognennyi most* (1976)
*On the Town* (1949)
*Opening the Williamsburg Bridge* (1904)
*Quatre nuits d'un rêveur* (1971)
*Sonnenstrahl* (1933)
*Sorcerer* (1977)
*Storstrømsbroen* (1950)
*Stroitsya most* (1965)
*Swiss Miss* (1938)
*Tarzan's New York Adventure* (1942)

*A Taste of Sin* (1983)
*Terminator 2: Judgment Day* (1991)
*The Thirty-Nine Steps* (1935)
*Under the Bridge* (1995)
*Vertigo* (1958)
*Volunteers* (1985)
*Waterloo Bridge* (1931, 1940)
*The Wild Bunch* (1969)
*Zerwany most* (1962)

The cable stays are sheathed in steel pipes 9 inches (23 cm) in diameter. This photograph shows the "bicycles," devices used to support and position the pipes into place. The pipes were eventually painted a brilliant taxicab yellow to increase the bridge's visual impact and, no doubt, play up its location in the Sunshine State.

*From an esthetic standpoint [the Sunshine Skyway Bridge] may well rank as the most impressive piece of large-scale bridge design in this country in half a century.*
—Paul Goldberger, The New York Times, October 46, 1988

Florida

Tampa Bay

St. Petersburg

**SUNSHINE SKYWAY**

Bradenton

# Sunshine Skyway Bridge

From a distance it looks like a futuristic schooner, sails aloft, barely skimming the surface of the water as it crosses Tampa Bay. Sometimes compared as well to the strings of a harp or an open fan, the triangular plane of stays that support the sleek Sunshine Skyway Bridge are, however described, a triumph of late-twentieth-century engineering design. Though not a new way of spanning the seas (cable-stayed bridges, relatively inexpensive and easily mounted on the piers of destroyed bridges, first gained popularity in post–World War II Germany), the Sunshine Skyway Bridge combines state-of-the-art engineering with a striking design that heralds the aesthetic possibilities of the cable-stayed bridge.

Completed in 1987, the bridge's 1,200-foot (366-meter)-long main span is the world's longest cable-stayed concrete span. In its entirety, including the side spans and approaches, the bridge is 21,878 feet (6,668 meters) long and crosses 4.1 miles (6.6 km) of Tampa Bay. Twin 40-foot (12-meter)-wide roadways run on either side of the cables and provide unobstructed views of the water. The roadways for the high level portion of the bridge are consticted of 330 95-foot (29-meter)-wide precast concrete segments that are

threaded with high-strength steel cables for the length of the bridge. This precast superstructure, in addition to being economical, provides continuous structural lines that contribute to the graceful appearance of the bridge. The twenty-one steel cables that support the roadway are splayed out in rows from two slender central pylons, which soar 242 feet (74 meters) above the deck. The cables are attached to every other deck segment, with each cable supporting two segments on either side of a pylon.

In its design and construction, the award-winning Sunshine Skyway Bridge has demonstrated the feasibility and economy of long-span cable-stayed bridges. In linking the communities of St. Petersburg and Clearwater in the north with Bradenton and Sarasota in the south, the bridge has fused the area surrounding Tampa into a whole, energizing it with new economic growth and, understandably, civic pride.

Two steel-truss bridges, built in 1954 and 1971, originally crossed Tampa Bay. The newer span was demolished on May 9, 1980, when the freighter *Summit Venture*, seen here with parts of the bridge on it, struck it during a violent thunderstorm, knocking out a 1,300-foot (396-meter) section, and killing 35 people. To deflect wayward ships from the skyway supports, concrete islands, or "dolphins," now protect the six piers surrounding the main shipping channel and can withstand the impact of an 87,000-ton (78,925-tonne) ship.

Tampa, a busy port and home to several major shipyards, needed a bridge of tremendous height to ensure that navigation would not be hindered. The roadway of the bridge soars 190 feet (58 meters) above the water.

| Crossing | Tampa Bay | Designer/Engineer | Figg Engineering Group | Completed | 1987 World's longest cable-stayed concrete span | Span | 1,200 feet/366 meters | Materials | concrete, steel | Type | cable-stayed |

*Perhaps the most striking of all the structures on the Kojima-Sakaide Route [are] the exactly-paired Hitsuishijima and Iwakurojima Bridges.... Only in Japan would there be towers of this shape, flaring outwards at the top in imitation, perhaps, of the helmets which were worn by medieval Japanese warriors.*
—David J. Brown, Bridges, 1993

The Hitsuishijima and Iwakurojima Bridges are twin cable-stayed bridges, the only such pairing in the world.

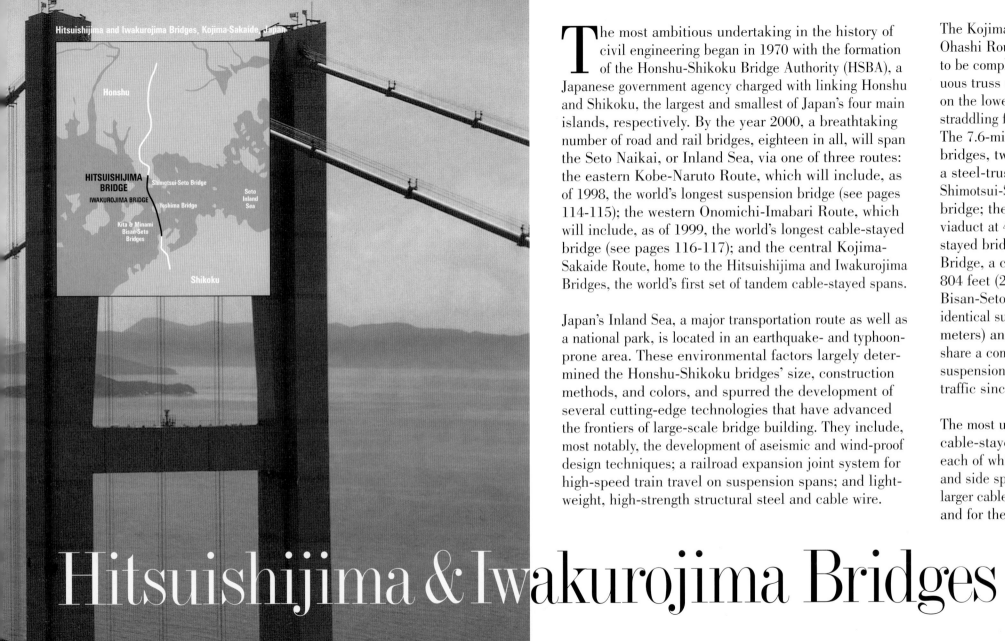

Hitsuishijima and Iwakurojima Bridges, Kojima-Sakaide, Japan

Honshu

HITSUISHIJIMA
BRIDGE

IWAKUROJIMA BRIDGE

Shimotsui-Seto Bridge

Yoshima Bridge

Kita & Minami
Bisan-Seto
Bridges

Seto
Inland
Sea

Shikoku

The most ambitious undertaking in the history of civil engineering began in 1970 with the formation of the Honshu-Shikoku Bridge Authority (HSBA), a Japanese government agency charged with linking Honshu and Shikoku, the largest and smallest of Japan's four main islands, respectively. By the year 2000, a breathtaking number of road and rail bridges, eighteen in all, will span the Seto Naikai, or Inland Sea, via one of three routes: the eastern Kobe-Naruto Route, which will include, as of 1998, the world's longest suspension bridge (see pages 114-115); the western Onomichi-Imabari Route, which will include, as of 1999, the world's longest cable-stayed bridge (see pages 116-117); and the central Kojima-Sakaide Route, home to the Hitsuishijima and Iwakurojima Bridges, the world's first set of tandem cable-stayed spans.

Japan's Inland Sea, a major transportation route as well as a national park, is located in an earthquake- and typhoon-prone area. These environmental factors largely determined the Honshu-Shikoku bridges' size, construction methods, and colors, and spurred the development of several cutting-edge technologies that have advanced the frontiers of large-scale bridge building. They include, most notably, the development of aseismic and wind-proof design techniques; a railroad expansion joint system for high-speed train travel on suspension spans; and lightweight, high-strength structural steel and cable wire.

The Kojima-Sakaide Route, popularly known as the Seto-Ohashi Route, was, in 1988, the first of the three routes to be completed. A strong 43-foot (13-meter)-deep continuous truss carries vehicles on the top deck and trains on the lower deck over a series of bridges and viaducts straddling five small islands between Kojima and Sakaide. The 7.6-mile (12.2-km) route consists of three suspension bridges, two cable-stayed bridges, three viaducts, and a steel-truss bridge. From south to north, they are: the Shimotsui-Seto, a 3,084-foot (940-meter)-span suspension bridge; the curving Hitsuishijima, the route's longest viaduct at 4,320 feet (1,317 meters); two identical cable-stayed bridges, which are discussed below; the Yoshima Bridge, a continuous truss viaduct with a main span of 804 feet (245 meters); the Yoshima Viaduct; the Kita Bisan-Seto and Minami Bisan-Seto bridges, two nearly identical suspension bridges with spans of 3,248 feet (990 meters) and 3,609 feet (1,100 meters) respectively, that share a common anchorage; and the Bannosu Viaduct. The suspension bridges are the first designed to carry railroad traffic since John Roebling's Niagara Bridge (1855).

The most unusual bridges on the route are the identical cable-stayed Hitsuishijima and Iwakurojima Bridges, each of which has a main span of 1,378 feet (420 meters) and side spans of 607 feet (185 meters). Although there are larger cable-stayed bridges, the duo is unique both as a pair and for their unprecedented deep-trussed double decks.

For more than 1,200 years, followers of the Buddhist prophet Kukai have made pilgrimages to Shikoku's eighty-eight sacred temples. As the last of the Honshu-Shikoku bridge links nears completion, devotees of long-span bridge technology will undoubtedly seek out Shikoku's secular wonders as well.

An aerial view of the Kojima-Sakaide Route shows, from front to back, the Kita Bisan-Seto Bridge, Yoshima Viaduct, Hitsuishijima and Iwakurojima Bridges, Hitsuishijima Viaduct, and Shimotsui-Seto Bridge.

# Hitsuishijima & Iwakurojima Bridges

| Crossing Seto Naikai (Inland Sea) | Designer/Engineer Honshu-Shikoku Bridge Authority | Completed 1988 | Span 1,378 feet/420 meters | Materials steel, concrete | Type cable-stayed |

*The supreme art of living is a consummation gained by no single calling and no single science; it is the yield of all occupations and all sciences, and many things besides.*

—José Ortega y Gasset, "Man the Technician," in Toward a Philosophy of History, 1941

Though Calatrava's work is structurally sound, it manages the simultaneous appearance of imminent flight or collapse. This quality is evident in the dynamic sweep of his Alamillo Bridge (1992) built adjacent to the Expo '92 exhibition site in Seville, Spain.

# Lusitania Bridge

As the twentieth century draws to a close, the Spanish-born, Zurich-based Santiago Calatrava (b. 1951) has emerged as the most inventive and controversial bridge builder now working. Trained as artist, architect, and engineer, Calatrava has, in a short time and with seeming disregard for the sacrosanct boundaries of contemporary architecture and engineering, cut a wide, exuberant swath in the built environment with constructions ranging from museums, train stations, libraries, warehouses, and bridges. The only thing predictable about Calatrava is his unpredictability.

The Lusitania Bridge connects the old section of the town of Mérida, Spain, with the newly developed area of Poligono on the northern side of the Guadiana River. The crossing consists of three parts: a steel arch that spans between arched concrete abutments and two concrete box girder side spans supported by a series of twin concrete piers. Just over 1,500 feet (457 meters) long, with an arch span of 620 feet (189 meters), the Lusitania is a small bridge, perfectly suited to the scale of the town it now graces. Calatrava's celebration of the human scale is also seen in the bridge's central pedestrian walkway, which, elevated above the roadways, provides unobstructed views of the river.

*Anything that is possible is permitted.*

—Santiago Calatrava, Lotus, 1992

The Lusitania's rotund piers have been criticized for their massive appearance, but perhaps they are an homage to La Alcazaba, the two-thousand-year-old Roman bridge less than a mile upstream, which it was built to replace. As pointed out by noted architectural historian Kenneth Frampton, Calatrava pays special attention to the context of his work and to the parts of a bridge that are usually invisible—its appearance from below as well as its reflection on the surface of the water—to underscore the plasticity and movement of the structure. Movement, the added dimension of every Calatrava project, is critical to his conception of his structures, which he likens to living things, such as "the sea that has waves that move, or…a flower whose petals open in morning."

What seems to gall Calatrava's critics most, although he is a qualified structural architect and engineer, is his audacious insistence on combining the roles of architect and engineer, two fields that were once—but emphatically no longer—one. Engineers are increasingly specialized, with most having a narrow, almost exclusively technical education and limited design experience, a condition exacerbated by the typical client, who wants the cheapest safe solution possible. In a field where there is perforce little design innovation or sense of cultural stewardship, Calatrava's daring and facility in a number of fields loom enviably large. His particular love of bridges—structures that bring together two sides that had previously been separate—is an apt and hopeful portent of the infrastructure's civic potential.

The Trinity Bridge in Salford-Manchester, Great Britain (1995), exhibits characteristics typical of Calatrava's bridges: a unique combination of construction materials; integration of the surrounding environment; awareness of the crossing as a regional landmark; and finally, the manipulation of lighting to emphasize the bridge's structural dynamic.

| Crossing Guadiana River | Designer/Engineer Santiago Calatrava | Completed 1991 | Span 620 feet/189 meters | Materials steel, concrete | Type arch and box girder |

*The environment called for a bridge with curved and slender shapes. We made our best effort to provide a signature precast concrete bridge for the Natchez Trace.*
—Gene Figg, President, Figg Engineering Group, 1997

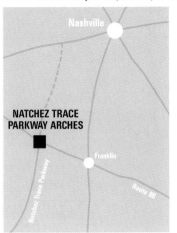

From wilderness path to modern parkway, the historic Natchez Trace has witnessed a colorful procession of humanity. Hernando de Soto, Andrew Jackson, Meriwether Lewis, and Ulysses S. Grant are but a few who traveled the Natchez Trace, or trail, between Tennessee and Mississippi. The 450-mile (720-km)-long path, carved through the woodlands centuries earlier by the Natchez, Choctaw, and Chickasaw tribes, remained a key military and trade route until the mid-eighteenth century.

To complete the Natchez Trace Parkway, a two-lane roadway along the historic thoroughfare, its owner, the National Park Service, wanted a simple arch bridge that would preserve the area's character and natural beauty. The resultant bridge, the Natchez Trace Parkway Arches, is a trailblazer in its own right.

# Natchez Trace Parkway Arches

The bridge's arches, decks, and piers were constructed of precast concrete segments, the first time precast segmental technology was used in an arched bridge in the United States. Designed by the Figg Engineering Group, the bridge roadway is borne on two arches spanning a large valley across Route 96 near Franklin, Tennessee, and three piers. The first arch is symmetrical, with a span of 582 feet (177 meters), and rises 145 feet (44 meters) over the highway; the second is asymmetrical, to accommodate the topography of the terrain, with a span of 462 feet (140 meters) and a 102-foot (31-meter) rise.

Typically, the superstructure of an arch bridge is supported by a number of evenly spaced vertical members called spandrels that distribute the weight of the superstructure on the arch. To create a lighter, more open, and visually pleasing structure, the Natchez Trace Parkway Arches were designed without spandrels, putting an unusual load on the arch crowns. To accommodate the load, the depth of the concrete boxes that form each arch was increased from ten to thirteen feet (three to four meters) as they approach the top of the arch and decreased back to ten feet (three meters) at the center of the arch.

To date, the Natchez Trace Parkway Arches has received eleven awards for its exemplary design. It has also been cited for an agreement reached early on among the National Park Service, Federal Highway Administration, and contractor to adopt a partnership approach to the project. By fostering an open climate for the discussion and settlement of issues, this approach influenced the completion of the bridge on schedule and without legal action, cost increases, or accidents.

Visually the bridge seems to leap through the woodlands with the swiftness and elegance of a greyhound. Constructed with an economy of materials and means, the innovative Natchez Trace Parkway Arches treads lightly indeed.

The arches are formed of hollow concrete segments that are threaded together with post-tensioning steel that is pulled through holes in the concrete and then anchored and tightened at the end of each span.

The Natchez Trace cuts through lands that were once part of a sophisticated trade network linking hundreds of ancient Native American communities throughout the Southeast. Many of these cultures constructed mounds for ceremony and/or burial that have yielded exotic treasures when excavated, such as this engraved marine shell ornament from Tennessee dating from the fourteenth century.

The arch halves were built toward each other in successive segments and supported by temporary cables until joined.

| Crossing | Tennessee Route 96 | Designer/Engineer | Figg Engineering Group | Completed | 1994 | Span | 582 feet/177 meters | Materials | concrete | Type | arch |
|---|---|---|---|---|---|---|---|---|---|---|---|
| | | | | | First precast concrete segmental arch bridge in the United States | | | | | | |

After a hundred years of closure the newly revealed Woonasquatucket (on the right) and Moshassuck rivers flow into the Providence River and empty into Narragansett Bay. Visible are the project's many bridges as well as a hurricane barrier in the distance.

*We have moved more than rivers. We have moved the heart and soul of a city.*
—Mayor Vincent "Buddy" A. Cianci, Jr., 1997

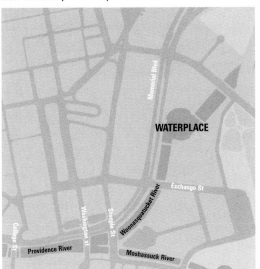

In 1636 Roger Williams and others seeking religious freedom settled in a propitious spot at the juncture of two freshwater rivers that merged and flowed out to the Atlantic. Williams, who had been deeded the land by Narragansett Indian chief Canonicus, named the spot "in commemoration of God's providence."

Providence's location made its fortunes flourish: its rivers were crucial commercial arteries serving the Atlantic coastal trade and mercantile exchange with the West Indies. The port gained further prominence during the American Revolution, when British troops closed the rival port of Newport, and it continued to grow into the early twentieth century, when manufacturing brought ships by the hundreds to the city's harbor. In a way unthinkable today, people dumped waste of every sort into the rivers until they were open sewers, fouling the air with their stench. The growing impulse was to cover them whenever possible.

Progress continued. In 1873 the 600-foot (183-meter)-wide Crawford Street Bridge was built over the Providence River to accommodate expanding markets, horse-drawn trolleys, and railroad lines. It was continually widened until 1940, when it made the *Guiness Book of World Records*

Eleven fires, mounted on the remnants of the Crawford Street Bridge, were part of "Water Fire," a 1996 multimedia piece by Barnaby Evans that celebrated the rebirth of the waterfront.

for its width of 1,147 feet (350 meters). By the 1970s the rivers were buried and downtown was derelict. Most people had forgotten that there had even been water there.

The waterfront was unearthed in a series of steps taken over a period of twenty years, beginning in 1978. The first step was to relocate the snarl of train tracks that held downtown a geographic captive, followed by the removal of the extended Crawford Street Bridge, and, finally and remarkably, the rivers themselves were moved in order to circumvent the Post Office built in 1940. This last feat involved carving out new riverbeds so that the confluence of the Moshassuck and Woonasquatucket rivers could be transferred to a site approximately 150 feet (46 meters) away.

Ultimately, under the direction of project architect William D. Warner, twelve pedestrian and vehicular bridges were erected. Faced with brick, granite, and textured concrete, the bridges have been designed to reflect the city's greatest treasure, the three centuries of architecture that surrounds them. The entire downtown area, in fact, is listed on the National Register of Historic Places; no other major city boasts such a distinction.

Eleven acres of riverfront parks, now alive with people, are dotted with places for music and theater. Gondolas began traversing the waterfront in the spring of 1997, joining a once unlikely stream of canoes, kayaks, swans, and fish. Three new museums have come to town and, given that artists living in a specially designated downtown arts zone pay no state income tax, more museums will undoubtedly follow. Indeed, in Providence, hope—the state's motto—has been reborn.

A 1939 aerial view shows how the rivers were literally paved over, earning the Crawford Street Bridge—actually eight contiguous bridges—dubious distinction as the world's "widest bridge."

# River Relocation, Providence

| Crossing | Moshassuck, Woonasquatucket, and Providence Rivers | Architect | William D. Warner | Completed | 1996 | Length | various | Material | concrete and steel | Type | arch |

*Through gaps in the urban fabric, the [Erasmus Bridge] slides unexpectedly into view, the hooked pylon grey-blue against the sky, the ultra-thin parapet sweeping towards terra firma.*
—Raymond Ryan, "Objective: Rotterdam," Blueprint, 1996

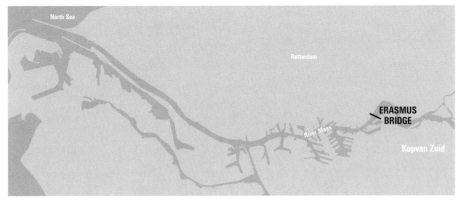

The 466-foot (142-meter)-high "knee-bend" pylon, now a point of orientation in the city, seems to announce the new developments in the Kop van Zuid area.

# Erasmus Bridge

The Erasmus Bridge, Ben van Berkel's glorious arching portal over the Maas River, operates as a vital connector between the two halves of the Dutch city of Rotterdam—the civic institutions on the river's north bank and the ambitious urban regeneration scheme known as the Kop van Zuid to the south. Its robust, asymmetrical form is actually three bridges in one. The combination—a cable-stayed bridge with a main span of 918 feet (280 meter), a side span viaduct, and a bascule bridge—indicates the multitude of urban, technical, and design considerations that figured in its construction.

Rotterdam, left a blank slate by World War II, has determinedly rebuilt itself, powered by a plan devised in 1946 for the reconstruction of its inner city. Contemporary architecture, high-rise buildings, wide boulevards, and the pioneering reuse of old harbor basins and quays are the hallmarks of the city today. Since its opening in September 1996, the Erasmus Bridge has presided over Rotterdam's energetic transformation.

The design of the sky-colored bridge presented a number of challenges. An enormous jigsaw of unique structural elements, the bridge contains virtually no straight angles. It would have been impossible to create and build the bridge without the help of modern computer technology, including three-dimensional, computer-aided simulation and calculation systems. The precocious van Berkel (b. 1961), an Amsterdam-based architect, designed the bridge, its lighting, and a number of its surrounding facilities. It was engineered by the City of Rotterdam's Department of Public Works.

Although most major harbor activities lie closer to the sea, there are still a number of shipbuilding and maintenance industries upstream from Rotterdam. Consequently, the harbor authorities required that the Erasmus Bridge have a navigational channel, which is provided by a remarkable single-leaf bascule bridge. Apart from its sheer size—with a 172-by-117-foot (52.4-by-35.7-meter) movable bridge deck, it is the largest of its kind in the world—there are other features that make this portion of the bridge unique. Most eye-catching is the oblique, 67-degree angle of the shipping channel: in its open position the parallelogram-shaped bridge deck tilts sideways, rather than straight up and down. To accommodate the public rail lines running over the bridge, the bascule also operates quickly, taking a total of four minutes to open and close.

According to van Berkel, the bridge's lighting plan was meant to emphasize its identity as both symbol and infrastructure. Indeed it is at night, when the massive bridge is transformed into an ethereal silhouette, its bundled cables now long strands of light, that one becomes most aware of the bridge's structure and the vital connecting role played by its daytime self.

Twenty thousand people a day cross the 108-foot (33-meter)-wide bridge deck, which carries twin tram lines for public transportation, two double traffic lanes, and free lanes for cyclists and pedestrians.

| Crossing | Maas River | Designer/Engineer | Ben van Berkel | Completed | 1996 | Span | 918 feet/280 meters | Materials | steel, concrete | Type | cable-stayed, viaduct, bascule |

On Oskoy Island Bridge, Bergen, Norway, 1994

Fatih Sultan Mehmet Bridge, Istanbul, Turkey, 1992

On the Royal Gorge Bridge, Colorado, 1989

With Joan on the Golden Gate Bridge, 1973

Top deck of Verrazano Narrows Bridge, New York, 1991

With the Ambassador (in white) on the Ponte 25 de Abril, Portugal, 1993

Donald Betty likes bridges, especially suspension bridges, and particularly the Golden Gate Bridge, which he has walked over five times. On a list Betty updates religiously, the Golden Gate is included, along with the Verrazano Narrows Bridge in New York and the Humber River Bridge in Hull, England. The list, better known as Exhibition Number One, names 101 more bridges, if you're counting. Betty is—and so is the *Guinness Book of World Records*, which for the past three years has cited Betty for walking across more suspension bridges than any-one else in the world, including the fourteen longest.

Betty, sixty-nine years young, worked for Bethlehem Steel during summer vacations from college. "Once you get steel in your blood," he says, "it stays there." He went on to earn a degree in mechanical, not civil, engineering, but bridges have always fascinated him. "I developed a tremendous feeling for people who designed these bridges and the bravery it took."

His bridge-walking hobby began quite accidentally in 1971, when he and Joan, his wife of forty-five years, were vacationing in Vancouver, British Columbia. On that trip Betty walked across his first suspension

bridge, the Capilano Canyon Bridge (a sentimental walk). Betty walked it again in 1997 on his 100th bridge walk). Two years later they visited San Francisco, and there was no turning back. "I fell in love with the Golden Gate Bridge. It was and is my absolute favorite for its history, its beauty, and what it took to build it," he says.

Why suspension bridges? "Because they are the biggest and most difficult bridges to build," answers Betty, and he points out that although he's from Lancaster, Pennsylvania, a place famous for its

covered bridges, he's never walked across one. He does, however, take boxes of Lancaster pretzels on his bridge walks to give to those who befriend him.

Sometimes he needs more than pretzels to cut through the red tape involved. "To cross most bridges, you need permission, and it can take months and months and a lot of political wrangling to get approvals." Some of the most difficult bridges are those closest to home. In order to cross the Verrazano Narrows Bridge, Betty waited until the day of the New York City Marathon, when he could walk over with the wheel-

On the Tsing Ma Bridge, Hong Kong, 1997

Waving from the top of the Delaware
Memorial Bridge, Delaware, 1994

On the Tsing Ma Bridge, Hong Kong, 1997

# No Bridge Too Far

chair participants prior to the crossing of the runners. Betty was getting nowhere trying to walk the Delaware Memorial Bridge, only sixty miles from his home, until he mentioned his problem to a friend who happened to cut the hair of the mayor of Bridgeton, New Jersey, who knew someone at the Delaware Port Authority. He crossed the Bosporus and Fatih Sultan Mehmet bridges in Istanbul under armed guard. "On the Angostura Bridge in Venezuela, we had to bribe the guards with 30,000 bolivares (about $15)," Betty recalls. By the time he got permission to cross the Ponte 25 de Abril in Lisbon, he had gotten to know

the U.S. ambassador to Portugal so well that the diplomat accompanied him across.

Other than a pair of Nikes, Betty has no special equipment. He has developed some rituals though. "I always pick up souvenirs from each bridge walk. I have quite a collection of washers, nails, coins, hubcaps, and windshield wipers from everywhere. I always lie down in the middle of the bridge and take a vertical shot of the tower. People ask, 'What's that man doing lying there?' It doesn't bother me. I get great pictures."

Mostly Betty walks alone, although Joan has joined him on about a third of his walks, as have his sons, Wayne and Clifford. It was Clifford who nominated his father, unbeknownst to Betty, for the Guinness book in 1994. ("Who's number two? Who cares!") Some of his most memorable walks have been taken with his grandchildren Amanda, Lauryn, Joshua, and Rebecca.

"Oh, I haven't mentioned that I had open heart surgery in 1990 and a total left knee replacement in 1991," the apparently indefatigable Betty recalls.

He adds that he doesn't suffer from gephyrophobia —a fear of bridges—but if you do, he recommends the Mackinac Bridge, where attendants will drive the terrified across.

What's next? "I crossed my 104th, the Tsing Ma Bridge in Hong Kong, on May 11, 1997. Next is the Corbin Bridge in Huntingdon, Pennsylvania, followed by the Höga Kusten in Sweden. I'll definitely be in Japan and Denmark in 1998, and China in 1999," Betty says. Wherever a new suspension bridge is being built, expect to see Donald Betty there sooner or later.

*We have touchdown.*
—Barry Guptill, hoist operator, on final
placement of a bridge girder, 1996

Massive chunks of ice moving across the strait could topple the bridge. To counter ice jamming against the piers during ice-out, the original distance between them was increased from 574 to 820 feet (152 to 250 meters).

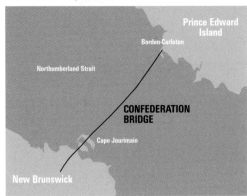

Prince Edward Island

Borden-Carleton

Northumberland Strait

**CONFEDERATION BRIDGE**

Cape Jourimain

New Brunswick

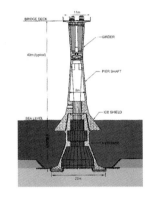

To avoid a structural catastrophe, the base of each pier, seen here in cross section, flares out so that the partially submerged ice shield forces ice floes to ride up the side of the pier and crack into pieces.

I n 1997 the Confederation Bridge, one of the world's longest continuous multispans opened, crossing the Northumberland Strait between Prince Edward Island and New Brunswick. The new bridge will substantially alter the island's relationship with the mainland as well as with the sea itself.

The builder, Strait Crossing, a consortium of Canadian, Dutch, and French firms, faced formidable natural and governmental obstacles in constructing the bridge. It is the only bridge of its class to be subjected to conditions as harsh as those prevailing in the frigid and windy strait. To meet federal criteria, the bridge has to stand for a hundred years without retrofit, twice as long as the normal lifetime of a bridge built in more hospitable climes.

With ice migrating back and forth across the strait for a good part of the year, a phalanx of engineers had to consider not only what would happen when ice encountered the bridge, but how the bridge might affect the flow of the ice. The big question, still unanswered, is whether the bridge will impede ice during ice-out, when the ice leaves the straits in the spring, and if it does, how local fisheries and agriculture will be affected.

The project's impact on the environment continues to be closely monitored; even the lobsters were considered—dredging of the sea bottom was timed to avoid the lobsters' peak molting season.

The bridge consists of 44 spans, which form 22 portals, in effect 22 individual bridges. Each of the main girders weighs 7,500 tons (6,804 tonnes) and measures 630 feet (192 meters), longer than two football fields. Placing the colossal girders down required hairbreadth precision and the loan of the *Svanen*, the giant swanlike (hence its Dutch name) crane used to construct the Great Belt Fixed Link in Denmark (see pages 112-113). The girders are joined by drop-in spans, which are alternately hinged to avoid a "progressive collapse," or domino effect, should the bridge be hit.

Ferry service, operating since 1917, ended the day before the bridge opened. For the nearly seven hundred former ferry employees, now receiving job retraining and stress counseling, the loss of the ferries is acute. For islanders and mainlanders alike, the opening of the bridge marks the passing of a way of life. While the Confederation Bridge has pioneered numerous, wondrous deep-ocean technological feats, its impact on human scale has yet to be measured.

Prince Edward Island, or Abegweit as it is called by the native Mi'Kmaq people, is increasingly inundated with tourists. The new bridge, which reduces the old forty-five-minute ferry crossing to a mere ten minutes, is expected to bring a million visitors a year to this province of 135,000.

# Confederation Bridge

*You never know what peace is until you walk on the shores or in the fields or along the winding red roads of Abegweit on a summer twilight when the dew is falling and the old, old stars are peeping out and the sea keeps its nightly tryst with the little land it loves.*
—Lucy Maud Montgomery, *Prince Edward Island*, 1939

| Crossing | Northumberland Strait | Designer/Engineer | Strait Crossing, Inc. | Completed | 1997 | Length | 8 miles/12.9 kilometers | Materials | concrete, steel | Type | concrete box girder |

The bridge's suspended roadway is supported by two reinforced-concrete towers. To resist the wind, the 656-foot (200-meter) towers were braced with steel trusses encased in concrete to form the permanent portal beams. Construction of the towers was interrupted briefly by typhoons.

**TSING MA BRIDGE**
Kowloon
Tsing Yi
Ma Wan Channel
Lantau Island
Hong Kong

# Tsing Ma Bridge

A spectacular fireworks display celebrated the opening of Hong Kong's Tsing Ma Bridge on April 27, 1997. In keeping with tradition, pedestrians were invited to walk over the bridge as soon as it was officially declared open by former British prime minister Margaret Thatcher. With a central span of 4,517 feet (1,377 meters) and designed to carry six lanes of traffic on its upper deck and two railways below, the Tsing Ma is the world's longest combined road and rail suspension bridge.

The Tsing Ma Bridge is the first land link between the Chek Lap Kok Airport now being developed just off Lantau Island and the rest of Hong Kong. The $900 million bridge is a key project in the government-sponsored $20 billion Airport Core Program to develop Hong Kong's infrastructure around the new international airport. Scheduled to open in April 1998, the airport will increase Hong Kong's air capacity from 24 to 35 million passengers per year, with a potential capacity of 87 million.

Over two miles (three km) long, the Lantau Link consists of the Tsing Ma Bridge, located between the islands of Tsing Yi and Ma Wan; the Ma Wan Viaduct, an elevated 2,296-foot (700-meter) viaduct that extends from the Tsing Ma Bridge across Ma Wan; and the Kap Shui Mun Bridge, a cable-stayed bridge with a 1,410-foot (430-meter) center span scheduled to open in 1997, that connects Ma Wan and Lantau.

The deck of the Tsing Ma is suspended from two main cables, each spun from 91 strands of 368 wires each. The cables pass over massive, 500-ton (454-tonne) steel saddles at the top of each tower. In an apropos sharing of construction duties, the primary steel for the deck was fabricated in Great Britain and Japan and shipped to a riverside assembly yard in Dongguan, China, fifty miles (eighty km) up the Pearl River from Hong Kong. A special barge was built to transport the deck sections two at a time—each is 118 feet (36 meters) long—to the bridge site, where they were lifted into their final position by gantries.

It is a fair bet that few future visitors to Hong Kong will miss the treacherous low flight over Kowloon City and daredevil landings on the narrow runway at the old Kai Tak Airport. Passengers will now arrive at a transparent

palace of an airport and be whisked over land and sea via the Tsing Ma. The bridge, completed just two months before the handover at midnight, June 30, is a big, if not elegant, signal of the changes in store for Hong Kong.

**Hong Kong, an international financial capital, was a British colony of six million people until it reverted to China, a nation of 1.2 billion.**

**The tower foundation on the Ma Wan side was constructed by submerging two caissons into a partially constructed artificial island. The completed island, visible at the base of the tower, protects the tower against collision by ships.**

*If there is a Chinese proverb, as surely there must be, contrasting the poverty of speech with the eloquence of action, it is a proverb that is constantly murmured by people in Hong Kong who are, because of their origins and their peculiar history, always mentally on the move.*
—Paul Theroux, "Memories That Drive Hong Kong," New York Times, 1997

| Crossing | Ma Wan Channel | Designer/Engineer | Mott MacDonald Hong Kong Limited | Completed | 1997 | Span | 4,517 feet/1,377 meters | Materials | steel, concrete | Type | suspension |

*The spinning wheels, bedecked with flags of the many nations participating in the project and cheered on by a jubilant ... the Storebælt to complete a world record performance for cable spinning and to finish some seven weeks ahead of schedule.*
—A/S Storebæltsforbindelsen press release, November 20, 1996

His Royal Highness Prince Joachim was the first person to pass through the southern tunnel tube in October 1994.

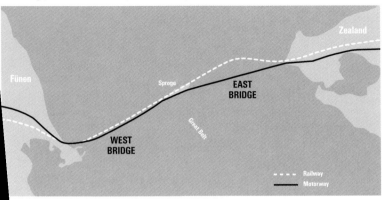

The main cables consist of almost 20,000 tons (18,144 tonnes) of wire, enough to circle the earth nearly three times. They were spun at an unprecedented rate of up to 285 tons (259 tonnes) per day over a period of 112 days by laborers recruited mainly from the ski-lift industry in the French Alps.

*rce, were set off on the 4,662nd and final trip across*

The $4 billion link now under construction across the 4.23-mile (6.77-kilometer)-wide Great Belt sound in Denmark is a bridge project of exceptional dimensions. The Great Belt, or Storebælt, Fixed Link consists of two bridges and a tunnel—the East Bridge, the West Bridge, and the Eastern Tunnel—that were built to improve Scandinavia's transportation network. The East Bridge, with a central suspended span of 5,326 feet (1,624 meters), will upset the respective world records of the Humber River and Mackinac bridges as the world's longest suspended span and longest overall suspended structure. But only for a brief moment. Within months of its completion in 1998, its record length will be surpassed by the astonishing Akashi Kaikyo Bridge with a central span of 6,527 feet (1,990 meters) now being built in Japan.

The link joins Denmark's two largest islands, Zealand and Fünen, via the tiny island of Sprogø. The longest suspension bridge ever constructed offshore, the East Bridge is a 4.2-mile (6.8-kilometer)-long steel vehicular bridge consisting of a central span, two 1,755-foot (535-meter) side spans, and 23 approach spans. Connecting Zealand (where the capital, Copenhagen, is located) and Sprogø, it was constructed by COINFRA, an international consortium of contractors. The West Bridge, completed in 1995, is a 4-mile (6.4-kilometer)-long prefabricated concrete bridge for cars and trains between Fünen and Sprogø. At Sprogø, the West Bridge rail and motorways split: the railway, completed in June 1997, continues on to Zealand via the East Tunnel, two parallel tubes nearly 5 miles (8 kilometers) long that were bored below bedrock between Zealand and Sprogø. The motor link from Sprogø to Zealand will open when the East Bridge is finished.

Before the East Bridge was built, various ship-maneuvering simulations were conducted to determine the type of design that would best accommodate the ships crossing the complex waters of the Great Belt, which is part of the international shipping route between the North Sea and the Baltic. Tests showed that a span of at least 5,248 feet (1,600 meters) was needed if the existing navigation route was to be unaffected. A cable-stayed design was studied but abandoned, because a 3,937-foot (1,200-meter) main span is, at present, the limit for a cable-stayed design. When safety and environmental considerations were factored into the final cost, a suspension bridge proved the most favorable solution.

In 1997 the construction of the East Bridge entered its final and most spectacular stage, the mounting of the cables and positioning of the bridge deck sections. The East Bridge is scheduled to open in June 1998.

The West Bridge terminates on the desolate island of Sprogø, formerly the site of a psychiatric patient facility. The area of the island has increased fourfold during construction, built up with earth dredged during construction.

# East Bridge, Great Belt Fixed Link

| ...sing | Great Belt | Designer/Engineer | COINFRA | Expected completion | 1998 | Span | 5,326 feet/1,624 meters | Materials | steel, concrete | Type | suspension |
|---------|------------|-------------------|---------|---------------------|------|------|-------------------------|-----------|-----------------|------|------------|

*There are certain memories of the past that have strong steel springs and, when we who live in the present touch them, they are suddenly stretched taut and then they propel us into the futur*
—Yukio Mishima, The Temple of the Golden Pavilion, 1956

Prefabricated circular steel caissons, each with a diameter of 240 feet (73 meters), were tugged to the site, submerged, and filled with regular concrete and a new silica fume concrete developed for this project.

Akashi Kaikyo Bridge, Honshu-Awaji, Japan

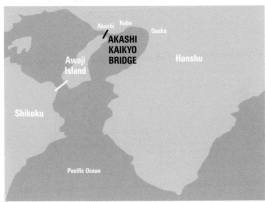

At 928 feet (283 meters), the bridge towers rival the heights of the Tokyo and Eiffel towers, are half again as tall as the massive Minami Bisan-Seto Bridge towers on the Kojima-Sakaide Route, and dwarf those of England's Humber River Bridge, which is currently the world's longest suspension bridge.

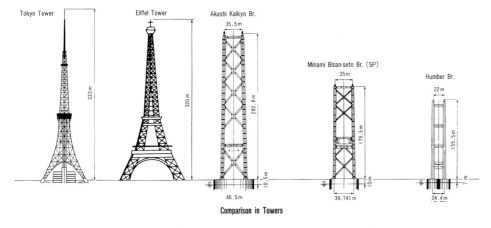

Comparison in Towers

# Akashi Kaikyo Bridge

It has been said that engineers at Japan's Honshu-Shikoku Bridge Authority (HSBA) "didn't want to challenge the gods" by adding ten meters to make the length of the Akashi Kaikyo Bridge's main span an even two kilometers. Still, the HSBA has managed to challenge almost every aspect of bridge design and construction in building eighteen major bridges on three routes that will hop islet to islet across the Seto Naikai, or Inland Sea, by the year 2000. Fourteen of the HSBA's collection of bridges are world-class spans, including the massive Tatara Bridge (see pages 116-117) and the idiosyncratic Hitsuishijima and Iwakurojima bridges (see pages 96-97). But the Akashi Kaikyo, with its record-breaking 6,527-foot (1,990-meter) suspended main span, is the group's crown jewel. When completed in 1998, the $7.6 billion structure will be the world's longest and most expensive suspension bridge.

The Akashi Kaikyo is on the Kobe-Naruto Route, the easternmost of the three new multibridge crossings, which links the islands of Honshu and Awaji. The route continues across Awaji Island to the Ohnaruto Bridge (1984), a 2,873-foot (876-meter) suspension bridge, and ends at Naruto on the island of Shikoku. Construction began in 1988. One of the last bridges to be completed, the 2.4-mile (3.8-km)-long Akashi Kaikyo has benefited from the experience engineers and contractors accumulated while building the earlier structures. Incredibly, no major bridges were built in Japan before 1973.

Bridge construction also benefited from advances in materials, the most notable of which was a high-strength steel wire never before used in a suspension span. The improved tensile strength of the cable wire permitted two, rather than four, main cables to be used.

Once the steel towers were in place, cable installation began. To avoid disrupting ship traffic—some 1,400 ships pass through the strait each day—a helicopter was used to install the pilot suspension rope in 1993. Subsequently, the HSBA prefabricated cables—bundling wires into strands off-site, then transporting them and pulling them from anchorage to anchorage—to improve on conventional spinning methods. On other decisions engineers stuck to the tried and true, just scaled up to fit the Akashi Kaikyo's Brobdingnagian dimensions.

1995 opened with a shock. On January 17, the magnitude 7.2 Great Hanshin Earthquake struck, devastating Kobe. Although the bridge was designed to withstand a magnitude 8.5 event, the epicenter of the quake was just six miles away. HSBA's initial relief to see the structure still standing gave way to anxiety when measurements indicated that the quake had pushed the towers three feet farther apart, enough to mean that the suspension hangers and deck needed redesigning. The month lost to the earthquake was regained when the erection of the deck's stiffening truss proceeded smoothly.

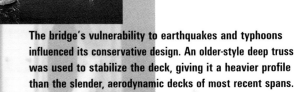

The bridge's vulnerability to earthquakes and typhoons influenced its conservative design. An older-style deep truss was used to stabilize the deck, giving it a heavier profile than the slender, aerodynamic decks of most recent spans.

| Crossing | Akashi Strait | Designer/Engineer | Honshu-Shikoku Bridge Authority | Expected completion | 1998 | Span | 6,527 feet/1,990 meters | Materials | steel | Type | suspension |
| --- | --- | --- | --- | --- | --- | --- | --- | --- | --- | --- | --- |
| | | | | Longest suspension span in the world | | | | | | | |

*The society of users, who are in fact willy-nilly the stewards of the world's bridges…must recognize that every artifact that has been or ever will be created, whether in now traditional steel and concrete or in the composites of the future, must be maintained as well as used.*
—Henry Petroski, Engineers of Dreams, 1995

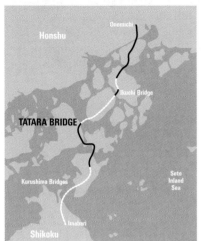

# Tatara Bridge

The cable-stayed Ikuchi Bridge (1991) is one of the six bridges already in use on the Onomichi-Imabari Route. It features two delta-shaped towers, from which planes of fan-arranged stays radiate. Constructed with composite girders, it has a 1,607-foot (490-meter) steel center span and 492-foot (150-meter) concrete side spans.

One of the last spans to be completed in the Honshu-Shikoku Bridge Authority's (HSBA) titanic building program will be the Tatara Bridge, shown here in a computer-generated montage. The Tatara is one of ten bridges on the Onomichi-Imabari Route, the westernmost of the three bridge routes between Honshu and Shikoku (see pages 96-97 and 114-115). With a central span of 2,919 feet (890 meters), the Tatara will be the world's longest cable-stayed bridge when it is completed in 1999.

In cable-stayed bridges, the deck is attached with cables directly to the pylons and supported by the cables, pylons, and onshore abutments, thus bypassing the need for the vertical suspenders, main cables, and anchorages of suspension bridges, which are the largest, most expensive type of bridge. Although the Tatara Bridge was originally conceived as a suspension bridge, a cable-stayed design was ultimately decided upon, because it is less costly and will be less invasive to the environment of the Seto Naikai, or Inland Sea, a national park.

The final link on the route will be completed the same year as the Tatara Bridge. This link—consisting of the Kurushima Bridges, three suspension bridges with main spans of 3,378 feet (1,030 meters), 3,346 feet (1,020 meters), and 1,968 (600 meters)—will be the only transportation facility in the world with three tandem suspension bridges.

Enthusiasm for the impressive scale of the HSBA bridge links has been tempered by the severe budget deficit and growing feeling among the Japanese that outsized public works such as these are consuming the country's wealth—Japan spends $300 billion annually on con-

struction—and bequeathing environmental devastation. According to a 1997 *New York Times* article by Andrew Pollack, the mood is one of reassessment, both of the need for construction of this magnitude and of the country's once-admired bureaucracy, now perceived as being riddled with corruption. Cutting back is proving to be difficult, however.

As the second millennium comes to a close, construction on a number of monumental bridges is under way, most notably in Norway, Sweden, China, and India. Engineers are pondering bold new bridge designs with both suspension and cable-stayed features capable of spanning once-improbable distances of more than 10,000 feet (3,048 meters). In light of infrastructure deterioration globally, however, many are urging that rehabilitation of older bridges, rather than construction of new ones, be funded.

The opening of a major bridge is a time to celebrate the vision, cooperation, and enormous ingenuity it represents. The specter that attends such celebrations, however, is that of the maintenance that bridges require throughout their lifetime. Unlike skyscrapers, their vertical counterparts, bridges are exposed structures and subject to daily onslaughts of traffic, wind, and weather that make them vulnerable to the life-threatening problems of stress fatigue and corrosion. While it is easy to hope that the problem of our neglected bridges will go away if ignored, many bridges are in dire need of rehabilitation. More than mere physical connections between two points of land, bridges serve as valuable links between societies, cultures, and political ideologies. As such they warrant our protection.

A March 1997 view of the construction of the deck of the Tatara Bridge.

| Crossing | Seto Naikai (Inland Sea) | Designer/Engineer | Honshu-Shikoku Bridge Authority | Expected completion | 1999 | Span | 2,919 feet/890 meters | Materials | steel, concrete | Type | cable-stayed |
| --- | --- | --- | --- | --- | --- | --- | --- | --- | --- | --- | --- |
| | | | | | Longest cable-stayed bridge in the world | | | | | | |

## Suspension

| Name | Location | Country | Year Completed | Main Span† Feet/Meters |
|------|----------|---------|----------------|------------------------|
| Akashi Kaikyo | Kobe-Naruto | Japan | 1998* | 6,527/1,990 |
| East Bridge, Great Belt Fixed Link | Fünen-Zealand | Denmark | 1998* | 5,326/1,624 |
| Humber | Hull | England | 1981 | 4,625/1,410 |
| Jiangrin | Yangtze River | China | 1997* | 4,543/1,385 |
| Tsing Ma | Hong Kong | China | 1997 | 4,517/1,377 |
| Verrazano Narrows | New York, NY | USA | 1964 | 4,260/1,298 |
| Golden Gate | San Francisco, CA | USA | 1937 | 4,200/1,280 |
| Höga Kusten | Veda | Sweden | 1997* | 3,969/1,210 |
| Mackinac | Straits of Mackinac, MI | USA | 1957 | 3,800/1,159 |
| Minami Bisan-Seto | Kojima-Sakaide | Japan | 1988 | 3,609/1,100 |
| Fatih Sultan Mehmet | Istanbul | Turkey | 1988 | 3,575/1,090 |
| Bosporus I | Istanbul | Turkey | 1973 | 3,523/1,074 |
| George Washington | New York-New Jersey | USA | 1931 | 3,500/1,067 |
| Kurushima III | Onomichi-Imabari | Japan | 1999* | 3,378/1,030 |
| Kurushima II | Onomichi-Imabari | Japan | 1999* | 3,346/1,020 |
| Ponte 25 de Abril | Lisbon | Portugal | 1966 | 3,323/1,013 |
| Forth Road | Queensferry | Scotland | 1964 | 3,300/1,006 |
| Kita Bisan-Seto | Kojima-Sakaide | Japan | 1987 | 3,248/990 |
| Severn | England-Wales | UK | 1966 | 3,240/988 |
| Shimotsui-Seto | Kojima-Sakaide | Japan | 1988 | 3,136/956 |
| Ohnaruto | Kobe-Naruto | Japan | 1984 | 2,873/876 |
| Tacoma Narrows | Tacoma Narrows, WA | USA | 1940 | 2,800/853 |
| Innoshima | Onomichi-Imabari | Japan | 1983 | 2,526/770 |
| San Francisco/Oakland Bay Bridge | San Francisco, CA | USA | 1936 | 2,310/704 |
| Bronx-Whitestone | New York, NY | USA | 1939 | 2,300/701 |

## Cable-Stayed

| Name | Location | Country | Year Completed | Main Span† Feet/Meters |
|------|----------|---------|----------------|------------------------|
| Tatara | Onomichi-Imabari | Japan | 1999* | 2,919/890 |
| Pont de Normandie | Le Havre | France | 1995 | 2,808/856 |
| Qingzhou Minjiang | Fuzhou | China | 1996 | 1,984/605 |
| Yangpu | Shanghai | China | 1993 | 1,975/602 |
| Xupu | Shanghai | China | 1997 | 1,935/590 |
| Meiko-Chuo | Nagoya | Japan | 1997 | 1,935/590 |
| Skarnsundet | Trondheim | Norway | 1991 | 1,738/530 |
| Tsurumi Tsubasa | Yokohama | Japan | 1994 | 1,673/510 |
| Ikuchi | Onomichi-Imabari | Japan | 1991 | 1,607/490 |
| Higashi-Kobe | Kobe | Japan | 1992 | 1,591/485 |
| Ting Kau | Hong Kong | Hong Kong | 1997 | 1,558/475 |
| Alex Fraser | Vancouver, BC | Canada | 1986 | 1,526/465 |
| Yokohama Bay | Yokohama | Japan | 1989 | 1,509/460 |
| Hoogly II | Calcutta | India | 1992 | 1,500/457 |
| Severn II | Bristol | England | 1996 | 1,496/456 |
| Rama IX | Bangkok | Thailand | 1987 | 1,476/450 |
| Queen Elizabeth II | Dartford-Thurrock | England | 1991 | 1,476/450 |
| Carlos Fernandez Casado | Barrios de Luna | Spain | 1983 | 1,444/440 |

## Steel Cantilever Truss

| Name | Location | Country | Year Completed | Main Span† Feet/Meters |
|------|----------|---------|----------------|------------------------|
| Québec | Québec City | Canada | 1917 | 1,801/549 |
| Forth | Queensferry | Scotland | 1890 | 1,710/521 |
| Nanko | Osaka-Amagasaki | Japan | 1974 | 1,673/510 |
| Commodore Barry | Chester, PA | USA | 1974 | 1,622/501 |
| Greater New Orleans | Louisiana | USA | 1958 | 1,575/480 |
| Greater New Orleans II | Louisiana | USA | 1988 | 1,575/480 |
| Howrah River | Calcutta | India | 1943 | 1,500/457 |
| Gramercy | Gramercy, LA | USA | 1995 | 1,460/445 |
| San Francisco/ Oakland Bay Bridge | San Francisco, CA | USA | 1936 | 1,400/427 |
| Baton Rouge | Baton Rouge, LA | USA | 1968 | 1,233/376 |

## Steel Arch

| Name | Location | Country | Year Completed | Main Span† Feet/Meters |
|------|----------|---------|----------------|------------------------|
| New River Gorge | Fayetteville, WV | USA | 1978 | 1,700/518 |
| Bayonne | New Jersey-New York | USA | 1931 | 1,652/504 |
| Sydney Harbor | Sydney | Australia | 1932 | 1,650/503 |
| Fremont | Portland, OR | USA | 1973 | 1,256/383 |
| Port Mann | Vancouver, BC | Canada | 1964 | 1,200/366 |
| Thatcher | Balboa | Panama | 1962 | 1,128/344 |
| Trois Rivières | Québec | Canada | 1967 | 1,099/335 |
| Runcorn-Widnes | Mersey River | England | 1961 | 1,082/330 |
| Zdákov | Lake Orlik | Czech Rep. | 1967 | 1,082/330 |
| Birchenough | Sabi River | Zimbabwe | 1935 | 1,079/329 |

*Expected completion date*

† *Main span length is the distance between a bridge's two principal supports.*

## Concrete Arch

| Name | Location | Country | Year Completed | Main Span† Feet/Meters |
|------|----------|---------|----------------|------------------------|
| Wanxiang | Yangzi River | China | 1996 | 1,378/420 |
| Krk I (east span) | Krk Island | Croatia | 1980 | 1,279/390 |
| Jiangjiehe | Wu River | China | 1995 | 1,082/330 |
| Yongjiang | Guangxi | China | 1996 | 1,023/312 |
| Gladesville | Sydney | Australia | 1964 | 1,000/305 |
| Amizade | Paraná River | Brazil/Paraguay | 1964 | 951/290 |
| Bloukrans | Van Stadens Gorge | South Africa | 1983 | 892/272 |
| Arrábida | Porto | Portugal | 1963 | 886/270 |
| Sandö | Kramfors | Sweden | 1943 | 866/264 |
| Chateaubriand | La Rance | France | 1991 | 856/261 |

## Steel Span Truss

| Astoria | Columbia River, OR | USA | 1966 | 1,233/376 |
|---------|--------------------|-----|------|-----------|
| Francis Scott Key | Baltimore, MD | USA | 1977 | 1,200/366 |
| Oshima | Yanai City-Oshima | Japan | 1976 | 1,066/325 |
| Kuronoseto | Akune City-Nagashima | Japan | 1974 | 984/300 |

## Concrete Box Girder

| Stolmasundet | Austevoll | Norway | 1998 | 987/301 |
|--------------|-----------|--------|------|---------|
| Raftsundet | Lofoten | Norway | 1998 | 977/298 |
| Humen | Pearl River | China | 1998 | 915/279 |
| Varodd | Kristiansand | Norway | 1994 | 853/260 |

## Steel Box Girder

| Name | Location | Country | Year Completed | Main Span† Feet/Meters |
|------|----------|---------|----------------|------------------------|
| Costa e Silva | Rio de Janeiro-Niteroi | Brazil | 1974 | 984/300 |
| Neckartalbruecke | Weitingen | Germany | 1978 | 863/263 |
| Sava I | Belgrade | Serbia | 1956 | 856/261 |
| Ponte de Vitoria III | Espirito Santo | Brazil | 1989 | 853/260 |

## Movable

| Arthur Kill | Elizabeth, NJ | USA | 1959 | 558/170 |
|-------------|---------------|-----|------|---------|
| al-Firdan | Suez Canal | Egypt | 1964 | 551/168 |
| Cape Cod Canal | Cape Cod, MA | USA | 1935 | 544/166 |
| Mississippi River | Fort Madison, IA | USA | 1927 | 525/160 |
| South Capitol Street | Washington, DC | USA | 1949 | 380/118 |

## Longest Overall Bridges/Trestles/Causeways

| Name | Location | Country | Year | Total Length Miles/Kilometers |
|------|----------|---------|------|-------------------------------|
| Lake Pontchartrain II | Metairie-Lewisburg, LA | USA | 1969 | 23.9/38.5 |
| Lake Pontchartrain I | Metairie-Lewisburg, LA | USA | 1956 | 23.8/38.3 |
| Chesapeake Bay | Chesapeake Bay, Virginia | USA | 1964 | 17.6/28.3 |
| King Fahd Causeway | Gulf of Bahrain | Bahrain-Saudi Arabia | 1986 | 15.5/24.9 |
| Sunshine Skyway | Tampa Bay, FL | USA | 1987 | 15.2/24.5 |
| Pinang | Pinang Island-Perai | Malaysia | 1985 | 8.6/13.8 |
| Confederation | Northumberland Strait | Canada | 1997 | 8/12.9 |
| Chesapeake Bay I | Chesapeake Bay, VA | USA | 1952 | 8/12.9 |
| Chesapeake Bay II | Chesapeake Bay, VA | USA | 1972 | 8/12.9 |
| San Mateo-Hayward | San Francisco Bay, CA | USA | 1967 | 7/11.3 |

# 100 Longest Bridges in the World by Type

Figures have been compiled from a number of sources, primarily documents provided by bridge contractors and state and federal transportation departments, as well as various engineering publications.

# Glossary

**Isambard Kingdom Brunel's Clifton Suspension Bridge, Bristol, England (1864)**

Abutment: the outermost end supports on a bridge, which carry the load from deck to ground.

Air-spinning: a method of constructing suspension bridge cables in which wires are unspooled back and forth across a span before being bundled into strands.

Anchorage: a block built on both ends of a suspension bridge, usually of concrete with embedded steel eyebars, to which the cables are fastened.

Aqueduct: an artificial channel for water, often elevated on arches.

Arch: a curved construction that spans an opening.

Bascule: a movable bridge span that opens upward by rotating on an axis, like a seesaw, with a counterbalance at the landside end.

Beam: a rigid, usually horizontal, member whose primary function is to carry a transverse load, i.e., a load that causes bending, as distinct from bowing or buckling.

Bicycle, or spinning carriage: a vehicle used in cable-spinning that lays the steel wires that are spun, or bundled, into a strand to form the main cable.

Box or plate girder: a hollow steel beam fabricated by welding, bolting, or riveting together metal sections in the form of a box that is designed to give strength without great weight.

Cable-stayed bridge: a bridge in which the deck load is carried by support cables radiating from a mast to a series of support points along the bridge deck.

Caisson: a prefabricated cofferdam used as a bridge foundation with sharp lower edges that cut into the riverbed, allowing it to sink down as excavation proceeds.

Cantilever: a projecting beam or member supported only on one end.

Cast iron: an alloy of iron and carbon that is shaped by being poured in its molten state into molds; notoriously unreliable in tension.

Catenary: the natural curve of a cable suspended from two towers.

Chord: a member at the top or bottom of a truss between which the vertical posts and diagonal braces are positioned.

Cofferdam: a temporary watertight dam that is used to construct a foundation by giving access to ground that is normally under water.

Compression: the stress resulting from a pushing force on a member, which tends to shorten it (the opposite of tension).

Formwork: the temporary system required to support and form concrete members.

Concrete: a mixture of pebbles, sand, cement, and water that hardens into a stonelike substance.

Cutwater: a pointed projection beyond the pier base that protects it by dividing the flow of water.

Dead load: the weight of a structure itself, including the weight of fixtures or equipment permanently attached to it.

Dynamic load: a load caused by wind that gives rise to vertical motion, creating vibrations in any direction.

Falsework: temporary framework used to support the incomplete parts of a bridge that cannot yet support themselves.

Girder: a large beam of steel, iron, reinforced concrete, or timber used to support concentrated loads at isolated points along its length.

Keystone: the stone that completes an arch, located in the center at the top.

Live load: the moving load on a structure, including the weight of people, cars, buildings, and equipment, but not including wind load.

Oscillation: the movement, usually vertical, of a suspended bridge deck in the wind.

Pier: the supporting structure between two or more arches or girders.

Pile: a structural element that is driven vertically into the ground to support a bridge. Pilings, or groups of piles, are used as a base on which to build abutments or piers.

Pneumatic caisson: a caisson with a compressed-air chamber.

Pontoon bridge: a bridge formed by floating flat-bottomed boats tied together and placing a roadbed on top.

Prestressed concrete: concrete that has been poured over stretched and anchored steel strands. After the concrete has set, the anchors are released; as the steel seeks to return to its original length it compresses the concrete, resulting in a lightweight, extremely strong material.

Pylon: a tower from which the chains or cables of a suspension or cable-stayed bridge are slung.

Reinforced concrete: concrete that has been hardened onto embedded metal, usually steel, in the form of rods, bars, or mesh. The tensile strength of steel and the compressional strength of concrete render a member capable of sustaining heavy stresses of all kinds over considerable spans.

Scour: the erosion of submerged piers from fast-flowing water.

Shear: the sliding of one layer of a material relative to another layer.

Span: the distance a bridge extends between two supports.

Spandrel: the triangular space between the side and crown of an arch.

Steel: an alloy of iron and carbon—graded according to the carbon content—that is equally strong in tension and compression.

Stiffening truss: a second length of steel or timber attached beneath the deck of a bridge to reinforce it against bending.

Suspension bridge: a bridge whose deck is supported from above by large cables or chains draped over vertical towers.

Swing bridge: a type of movable bridge that opens by swinging the deck to one side.

Tension: the stress resulting from a pulling force on a member, which tends to extend it (the opposite of compression).

Torsion: a force action that twists a member.

Truss: lengths of timber, iron, or steel framed together, usually in the form of triangles, to bridge a space economically without bending.

Two-hinged arch: an arch that is hinged at the abutments only.

Vertical lift bridge: a bridge that opens by raising the entire bridge deck in one piece between two towers.

Voussoir: the wedge-shaped masonry blocks from which an arch is formed.

Wrought iron: a malleable alloy with a very low carbon content that has high tensile strength and low compressive strength.

# Bibliography

**Books**

Ammann, O. H., Theodore von Kármán, and Glenn B. Woodruff. *The Failure of the Tacoma Narrows Bridge.* Washington, D.C.: Federal Works Agency, 1941.

Andric, Ivo. *The Bridge on the Drina.* Translated by Lovett Edwards. New York: Macmillan, 1959.

Beckett, Derrick. *Bridges.* London: Paul Hamlyn, 1969.

Bluestone, Daniel. *Constructing Chicago.* New Haven: Yale University Press, 1991.

Bohn, David, and Rodolfo Petschek. *Kinsey, Photographer.* San Francisco: Chronicle Books, 1984.

Bill, Max. *Robert Maillart.* New York: Praeger, 1969.

Billington, David P. Robert *Maillart's Bridges: The Art of Engineering.* Princeton, N.J.: Princeton University Press, 1979.

————.*The Tower and the Bridge: The New Art of Structural Engineering.* New York: Basic Books, 1983.

————. *Robert Maillart and the Art of Reinforced Concrete.* New York and Cambridge, Mass: Architectural History Foundation and MIT Press, 1990.

Boyer, Marjorie Nice. *Medieval French Bridges: A History.* Cambridge, Mass: The Medieval Academy of America, 1976.

Brooklyn Museum. *The Great East River Bridge.* New York: Harry N. Abrams, 1983.

Brown, David, J. *Bridges.* New York: Macmillan, 1993.

Captiman, Barbara, Michael D. Kinerk, Dennis W. Wilhelm. *Rediscovering Art Deco U.S.A.* New York: Viking Studio Books, 1994.

Condit, Carl, W. *American Building.* Chicago: University of Chicago Press, 1968.

Cortright, Robert, S. *Bridging.* Tigard, Ore.: Bridge Ink, 1994.

DeLony, Eric. *Landmark American Bridges.* Boston: Little Brown, 1993.

DeMaré, Eric. *Bridges of Britain.* London: Batsford, 1975.

Eisenhower, Dwight D. *Crusade in Europe.* New York: Doubleday, 1990.

Frampton, Kenneth. *Modern Architecture: A Critical History.* London: Thames & Hudson, 1985.

Frampton, Kenneth, Anthony C. Webster, and Anthony Tischhauser. *Calatrava: Bridges.* Zurich: Artemis, 1993.

Giedion, Sigfried. *Space, Time and Architecture.* Cambridge, Mass.: Harvard University Press, 1980.

Gies, Joseph. *Bridges and Men.* New York: Grosset & Dunlap, 1963.

Griggs, Francis E., Jr., ed. *A Biographical Dictionary of American Civil Engineers.* New York: American Society of Civil Engineers, 1991.

Hechler, Ken. *The Bridge at Remagen.* New York: Ballantine Books, 1957.

Hegel, Georg Wilhelm Friedrich. *The Philosophy of History.* New York: Dover, 1956.

Hicks, Frederick C. *High Finance in the Sixties: Chapters from the Early History of the Erie Railway.* New Haven: Yale University Press, 1929.

Hopkins, H. J. *A Span of Bridges.* New York: Praeger, 1970.

Hungerford, Edward. *Men of Erie.* New York: Random House, 1946.

James, Henry. *Italian Hours.* New York: Horizon Press. 1968.

Janson, Peter. *The Providence Waterfront: Three Centuries of Commerce.* Providence: Providence Preservation Society, 1983.

Johnson, Roger. *New City, Old Bridge.* Lake Havasu City, Ariz.: Media Specialist, 1981.

Knapp, Ronald G. *Chinese Bridges.* New York: Oxford University Press, 1993.

Kostof, Spiro. *A History of Architecture: Settings and Rituals.* London: Oxford University Press, 1985.

Le Corbusier. *When Cathedrals Were White.* New York: Reynal & Hitchcock, 1947.

Leonhardt, Fritz. *Bridges: Aesthetics and Design.* Cambridge, Mass.: MIT Press, 1984.

Lewis, R.W.B. *The City of Florence: Historical Vistas & Personal Sightings.* New York: Farrar, Straus & Giroux, 1995.

Lowe, Jet. *Industrial Eye.* Washington, D.C.: Preservation Press, 1986.

Loyrette, Henri. *Gustave Eiffel.* New York: Rizzoli International, 1985.

McCullough, David. *The Great Bridge.* New York: Simon and Schuster, 1972.

Mishima, Yukio. *The Temple of the Golden Pavilion.* Tokyo and Rutland, Vermont: Charles E. Tuttle, 1989.

Moore, Charles, and Jane Lidz. *Water and Architecture.* New York: Harry N. Abrams, 1994.

Morris, James. *The World of Venice.* New York: Pantheon Books, 1960.

O'Connor, Colin. *Historic Bridges of Australia.* Queensland: University of Queensland Press, 1985.

———. *Roman Bridges.* Cambridge, Great Britain: Cambridge University Press, 1993.

Ortega y Gasset, José. *Toward a Philosophy of History.* New York: W. W. Norton, 1941.

Petroski, Henry. *To Engineer is Human: The Role of Failure in Successful Design.* New York: St. Martin's Press, 1982.

———. *Engineers of Dreams; Great Bridge Builders and the Spanning of America.* New York: Alfred A. Knopf, 1995.

Plowden, David. *Bridges: Spans of North America.* New York: Viking Press, 1974.

Pritchett, V. S. *London Perceived.* New York: Harcourt, Brace & World, 1962.

Reavis, L. U. *A History of the Illinois and St. Louis Bridge.* St. Louis: Tribune Publishing, 1874.

Reed, Henry Hope, Robert M. McGee, and Esther Mipaas. *Bridges of Central Park.* New York: Greensward Foundation, 1990.

Richards, J. M. *The National Trust Book of Bridges.* London: Jonathan Cape, 1984.

Rousseau, Jean-Jacques. *The Confessions of Jean Jacques Rousseau.* New York: Modern Library, 1945.

Ruskin, John. *The Stones of Venice.* Boston: Little, Brown, 1981.

Russell, John. *Paris.* New York: Harry N. Abrams, 1983.

Sayenga, Donald. *Ellet and Roebling.* York, Penn.: American Canal and Transportation Center, 1983.

Schodek, Daniel L. *Landmarks in American Civil Engineering.* Cambridge, Mass.: MIT Press, 1987.

Scott, Quinta, and Howard S. Miller. *The Eads Bridge.* Columbia, Mo.: University of Missouri Press, 1979.

Shanor, Rebecca Read. *The City That Never Was: Two Hundred Years of Fantastic and Fascinating Plans That Might Have Changed the Face of New York City.* New York: Viking Penguin, 1988.

Steinman David B., with John T. Neville. *Miracle Bridge at Mackinac.* Grand Rapids, Mich.: William B. Eerdmans, 1957.

Steinman David, B., and Sara Ruth Watson. *Bridges and Their Builders.* New York: G. P. Putnam's Sons, 1941.

Stern, Robert A. M. *New York 1930: Architecture and Urbanism Between the Two World Wars.* New York: Rizzoli, 1995.

Stern, Robert A. M., Thomas Mellins, and David Fishman. *New York 1960: Architecture of Urbanism Between the Second World War and the Bicentennial.* New York: Monacelli Press, 1995.

Strauss, Joseph B. *The Golden Gate Bridge: Report of the Chief Engineer to the Board of Directors of the Golden Gate Bridge and Highway District.* San Francisco, Calif.: Golden Gate Bridge and Highway District, 1938.

Trachtenberg, Alan. *Brooklyn Bridge: Fact and Symbol.* New York: Oxford University Press, 1965.

Turner, Jane, ed. *The Dictionary of Art.* London: Grove, 1996.

Vitruvius. *De Architectura.* Cambridge: Harvard University Press, 1988.

Vogel, Robert M. *Roebling's Delaware and Hudson Canal Aqueducts.* Washington, D.C.: Smithsonian Institution Press, 1971.

Warner, William D. *The Providence Waterfront 1686–2000.* Providence: Providence Foundation, 1985.

———. *I-195 Old Harbor Plan 1992.* Providence: City of Providence, State of Rhode Island, Providence Foundation, 1992.

Watson, Wilbur J. *Bridge Architecture.* New York: William Helbrun, 1927.

Weigold, Marilyn E. *Silent Builder: Emily Warren Roebling and the Brooklyn Bridge.* Port Washington, N.Y.: Associated Faculty Press, 1984.

Whitman, Walt. *Leaves of Grass.* New York: New American Library, 1958.

Whitney, Charles S. *Bridges: A Study in Their Art, Science and Evolution.* New York: William Edwin Rudge, 1929.

Wilder, Thornton. *The Bridge of San Luis Rey.* New York: Harper & Row, 1927.

Winpenny, Thomas R. *Without Fitting, Filing, or Chipping: An Illustrated History of the Phoenix Bridge Company.* Easton, Penn.: Canal History and Technology Press, 1996.

Woodward, Calvin. *A History of the St. Louis Bridge.* St. Louis: G.I. Jones, 1881.

### Articles
Reference includes numerous reports, reprints, news releases, and brochures published by contractors and developers, government transit authorities, and state departments of engineering, public works, and transportation.

Adams, Nicholas. "Architecture as the Target." *Journal of the Society of Architectural Historians* 52 (Dec. 1993.): 389–90.

Beazley, Elizabeth. "The Menai Suspension Bridge and Britannia Bridge." *Ancient Monuments Society Transactions* 29 (1985): 36–62.

Bethlehem Steel Company. "The Golden Gate Bridge." Bethlehem, Penn., 1937.

Braet, Jan. "Jigsaw Rialto." *Archis* (Dec. 1993): 9.

Brown, Ivor J. "The Lloyds, Ironbridge, Shropshire: Some Aspects of a Nineteenth Century Mining Community." *Industrial Archaeology Review* 14 (Autumn 1991): 5–16.

Brussat, David. "The Crawford Street Bridge." *Providence Journal-Bulletin*, March 28, 1996, B7.

Buchanan, Peter. "Expressive Engineering: Calatrava." *Architectural Review* 182 (Sept. 1987): 50–61.

Buckley, Tom. "The Eighth Bridge." *The New Yorker*, Jan. 14, 1991, 37–59.

Cooper, Theodore. "American Railroad Bridges." *Transactions of the American Society of Civil Engineers* 99 (1934): 314–408.

DeLony, Eric. "HAER's Historic Bridge Program." *The Journal of the Society for Industrial Archeology* 15 (1989): 57–71.

DeLony, Eric, ed. "Historic Bridge Bulletin." *Society for Industrial Archeology* 1 (Summer 1984): 1–8.

Dethier, Jean. "Past and Present of the Inhabited Bridge." *Rassegna* 13 (Dec. 1991): 10–19.

Doig, Jameson W. "Politics and the Engineering Mind: O. H. Ammann and the Hidden Story of the George Washington Bridge." *Urban Affairs Annual Review* 43 (1995): 21–70.

Figg, Eugene C., and Charles F. Duggan. "Precast Segmental Bridge Solutions—the Past Ten Years." *Pittsburgh Engineer* (May/June 1993): reprint.

Gibbon, Michael. "Stowe, Buckinghamshire: The House and Garden Buildings and Their Designers." *Architectural History* 20 (1977): 31–44.

Gilmour, Ross, Gerald Sauvageot, Daniel Tassin, and James D. Lockwood. "Snaking Across the Strait." *Civil Engineering* (Jan. 1997): reprint.

Goldberger, Paul. "A Breathtaking Bridge Soars High over Tampa Bay." *New York Times*, Oct. 16, 1988, H36.

Goldstein, Harry. "Triumphant Arches." *Civil Engineering* (July 1995): reprint.

Heffner, Stephen. "The New Face of Providence." *Providence Sunday Journal*, Nov. 3, 1996, I1–6.

Hodson, Harry. "The Iron Bridge: Its Manufacture and Construction." *Industrial Archaeology Review* 15 (Autumn 1992): 36–44.

Hybels, Lynne. "The Old Bridge." *Willow Creek Monthly* (May 1996):1–3.

Insolera, Italo. "Viaduc de Garabit." *Zodiac* 13 (1964): 91–115.

Iovine, Julie V. "Will Bridges Be the Next Frontier?" *New York Times*, Nov. 21, 1996, C8.

Jackson, Donald C. "Nineteenth Century Bridge Failures: A Professional Perspective." *Proceedings of the Second Historic Bridges Conference* (March 1988): 113–24.

Janofsky, Michael. "Providence is Reviving: Using Arts as the Fuel." *New York Times*, Feb. 18, 1997, A14.

Kaufman, Michael T. "A Bridge over Bosnia's Desperation." *New York Times*, July 7, 1992, 6.

Kemp, Emory L. "The Fabric of Historic Bridges." *The Journal of the Society for Industrial Archeology* 15 (1989): 3–21.

Knapp, Ronald G. "Bridge on the River Xiao." *Archaeology* 41 (Jan.-Feb. 1988): 48–54.

Kouwenhoven, John A. "Eads Bridge: The Celebration." *Missouri Historical Society Bulletin* 3 (April 1974): 159–80.

La Monaca, Luigi. "Precast Concrete Segments." *L'Industria Italiana del Cemento* 12 (Dec. 1996): 834–47.

Logan, William Bryant. "The Gothic According to Calatrava: Completion of the New York Cathedral." *Lotus International* 72 (1992): 64–69.

McVicar, D. Morgan. "Providence Renaissance." *Providence Journal-Bulletin*, June 21, 1996, B1–8.

Maguire, Robert, and Peter Matthews. "The Ironbridge at Coalbrookdale: A Reassessment." *Architectural Association Journal* 74 (July-August 1958): 31–45.

Margolis, Richard, and Tom Peters. "Bridges—Symbols of Progress." Roland Gibson Gallery and Lehigh University Art Galleries exhibition catalog, 1991.

"Michigan Avenue Bridge." *Report of the Commission on Chicago Historical and Architectural Landmarks* (1982): 73–81.

Morgan, Thomas J. "Bridge to the Past." *Providence Journal-Bulletin*, March 18, 1996, C1.

Murray, Peter. "Life on the Water: Habitable Bridge." *Blueprint* (Oct. 1996): 13–22.

Petersen, Anton, and Lars Hauge. "European Long Span Bridges: A State-of-the-Art Report." *Civil Engineering Practice* 10 (Fall/Winter 1995): 43–54.

Pieper, Jan. "Palladian Bridges." *Daidalos* 57 (Sept. 15, 1995): 88–93.

Pierson, John. "Bridge Designs Go to Improbable Lengths." *Wall Street Journal*, Feb. 22, 1996, B1.

Pollack, Andrew. "Japan's Road to Deep Deficit Is Paved with Public Works." *New York Times*, March 1, 1997, A1.

Rastorfer, Darl. "Six Bridges: The Making of the New York Megalopolis." PaineWebber exhibition catalog, 1996.

Rombly, Giuseppina Carla. "Monuments." *Rassegna* 13 (1991): 59–60.

Schuyler, Montgomery. "The Bridge as a Monument." *Harpers Weekly*, May 26, 1883.

Sibly, P. G., and A. C. Walker. "Structural Accidents and Their Causes." *Proceedings of the Institution of Civil Engineers* 62 (1977): 191–208.

Soast, Allen. "Skyway Bridge Boasts a Record and Innovations." *Engineering News Record* (Sept. 1986): reprint.

Stewart, Doug. "Transforming the Beauty of Skeletons Into Architecture." *Smithsonian* (Nov. 1996): 76-85.

Sudetic, Chuck. "Mostar's Old Bridge Battered to Death." *New York Times*, Nov. 11, 1993, 18.

Theroux, Paul. "Memories That Drive Hong Kong." *New York Times*, June 10, 1997, A23.

Thurston, Harry. "Strait Across." *Canadian Geographic* (March/April 1997): 53–60.

"The Tower Bridge." *The Builder* 66 (June 30, 1894): 491–92.

"Venezuela Opens 5.5-Mile Span Called a Key to Economic Gains." *New York Times*, Aug. 25, 1962, 8.

Vesterhold, Jorgen. "Bridging of the Great Belt, and the Landscape." *Landskab* 1 (1991): 24.

Vincentsen, Leif J., and Kjeld Roger Henriksen. "Denmark Spans Strait with Great Belt Link." *Concrete International: Design and Construction* 14 (July 1992): 25–29.

Webster, Anthony C. "Utility, Technology and Expression." *Architectural Review* 191 (Nov. 1992): 68–74.

Westhofen, W. "The Forth Bridge." *Engineering* (Feb. 28, 1890): 213–83.

Wiley, Bud. "Above It All." *Life* (Feb. 1995): 84–85.

## Websites

With the exception of addresses that start with http://, websites are preceded by http://www.

best.com/~solvers/bridge.html (SC Solutions, Bridge Engineering Page)

dot.ca.gov/dist4/sfobbrto.html (Seismic Retrofit of San Francisco/Oakland Bay Bridge)

civeng.carleton.ca/ECL/reports/ECL270/Disaster.html (Québec Bridge Disaster)

clpgh.org/exhibit/exhibit.html (Bridging the Urban Landscape, Carnegie Library of Pittsburgh)

cr.nps.gov/habshaer/database.htm (Historic American Building Survey/Historic American Engineering Record Database)

cybercity.hko.net/hongkong/gakei/bridge.htm (Tsing Ma Bridge)

ggb60.com/ (Golden Gate Bridge 60th Anniversary page)

greatbelt-as.dk/ (Great Belt Link Home Page)

hero.or.jp/hero/index.html (Kobe & Hanshin-Awaji Economic Revitalization News)

hsba.go.jp/e-index.htm (Honshu-Shikoku Bridge Authority)

http://204.189.12.10/Goldengate/index.html (Golden Gate Bridge, California Highway and Transportation District)

http://arcweb.sos.or.gov/coast/OregonCoastWelcome.html (Oregon Coast Highway)

http://home.sprynet.com/sprynet/shig/japane.htm (Bridges in Japan)

http://william-king.www.drexel.edu/top/bridge/cb1.html (A Guide to Old Covered Bridges)

inventionfactory.com/history/main.html (John A. Roebling & Sons History Archive)

lexmark.com/data/poem/hcrane01.html (Hart Crane)

peinet.pe.ca/SCI/bridge.html (Confederation Bridge)

sfmuseum.org/1906/89.html (1989 Collapse of Oakland Bay Bridge)

# Index

# Acknowledgments

Of the many people who helped shape this book, I am most indebted to Ted Goodman at the Avery Library at Columbia University, who reviewed the text and prepared the index, and Jacqueline Decter, who edited the manuscript. For their skill, friendship, and commitment to this project, I am grateful.

This book has been enriched by the talent and invaluable contributions of Elizabeth Abbott and Medwyn Parry. Eric DeLony, David Plowden, Bob Cortright, and Erica Stoller, in particular, generously shared their knowledge with me, and the text reflects their helpful suggestions. This book rests on the scholarship of many others as well, and I list their works in the bibliography with appreciation. My assistants, Laura Tatum and Laura Kreiss, dug deep on my behalf, and I am grateful for their thoroughness. The many letters I received from readers of *Skyscrapers*, the first book in this series, were a source of joy and new ideas. My thanks to all of you.

I wish to thank everyone at Black Dog & Leventhal, particularly Pam Horn, Tim Stauffer, Helene Liss, Justin Lukach, and especially J. P. Leventhal for his enthusiasm and vision. As always it was a pleasure to collaborate with Alleycat Design.

Jane Gaffney, Patricia Finnegan, and Claire Nicita lovingly cared for my sons, Brendan and Emmet, so I could work without worry. My husband, Harry Gaffney, ever the cornerstone, provided understanding, love, and encouragement for the duration of this project.

Many others shared their expertise and resources with me. I am particularly grateful to the following individuals for their contributions:

Dr. Margot Ammann-Durer;
Gretchen Bank, Ted Strand, and John Zills, Skidmore, Owings & Merrill;
Bonnie Barsness, Lake Havasu City Visitors & Convention Bureau;
Donald and Joan Betty;
David Billington, Princeton University;
Ken and Cara Blazier;
Dave Bohn;
Lazlo Bodo;
Sandor Bodo;
Rollie Carrillo, Lake Havasu Tourism Bureau;
Vincent "Buddy" A. Cianci, Mayor, City of Providence;
Christo and Jeanne-Claude;
Jocelyn Clapp, Corbis-Bettmann;

Judy Clark, Delys de Zwaan, and the staff at the Mamaroneck Public Library;
Thaddeus and Susan Cook;
Weiping Dai;
Jeanmaire Dani;
Thomas Deller and Kathryn Cavanaugh, Department of Planning & Development, City of Providence;
B. J. and Melanie Dupré;
Peter and Lisa Dupré;
Susan Dupré;
the staff at Esto Photographics;
Andy Farenwald;
Eugene Figg and Jean Connolly, Figg Engineering Group;
Kenneth Frampton, Columbia University;

Brian Fulcher;
Neil Goodwin, Peace River Films;
Alan Gottlieb;
Mark Griffin;
Robert Hadlow, Jeff Swanstrom, and Orrin Russie, Oregon Department of Transportation;
Barbara Hall, Jon Williams, Carol Lockman, and the staff of the Hagley Museum and Library;
Patrick Harbron;
Patrick Harshbarger, Society for Industrial Archeology;
Dean Herrin, National Park Service;
Stan Kaderbek and Lou Chrzasc, Chicago Department of Transportation;
Ann Kilbourne;
Joseph Ka-Kee Lee;
Ellen Lederer and Alex Wesman;
Marianne Letasi, Detroit Institute of Arts;
Robert Loffredo;
Roger A. McCain, Drexel University;

Brian MacLean, Thomas Allen & Sons;
Richard Margolis;
Beth and Ed Matthews;
Linda Norris and Robert Parsons, Michigan Department of Transportation;
Regina Clarkin O'Leary;
Janet Parks and Dan Kany, Avery Architectural Library, Columbia University;
Frank Pascual, MTA Bridges and Tunnels, New York;
Catha Grace Rambusch;
Darl Rastorfer;
Ada Rodriguez;
Herb Rothman and Helen Oppenheimer, Weidlinger Associates, Inc.;
Brenda Tharp;
William D. Warner;
Robert and Cynthia Wilson;
Dennis S. M. Wong, Lantau Fixed Crossing Project;
and William Worthington, Smithsonian Institution, Division of Engineering and Industry.

# Illustration Sources

All images are copyrighted by the photographers and in some instances by the lending institutions. Images not credited are in the public domain or from the collection of the author.

t = top; l = left; r = right; tl = top left; tr = top right; c = center; cl = center left; cr = center right; b = bottom; br = bottom right.

Agence France Presse/Corbis-Bettmann: 24 (inset);
Alinari/Art Resource, New York: 17r, 22, 26, 33br;
Dr. Margot Ammann-Durer: 73l;
Wayne Andrews/Esto Photographics: 27tr, 34, 52;
Avery Architectural and Fine Arts Library, Columbia University in the City of New York: 35l, 39r, 46, 52 (inset), 53;

Alex Bartel/Esto Photographics: 62, back cover (c);
Donald Betty: 106, 107;
David Billington, Princeton University: 70, 71l;
Sandor Bodo: 102, 103l;
Boily Place: 108, 109r;
Richard Bryant, Esto/Arcaid: 13l, 13r, 104, 105, back cover (b);
Gary Taber, Copelin Photographics/Chicago Department of Transportation, Bureau of Bridges and Transit: 68, 69r;
Chicago Department of Transportation, Bureau of Bridges and Transit: 69br;
Corbis-Bettmann: 13cl, 16 (inset), 31l, 44, 45, 56, 57l, 68 (inset), 72, 78, 120;

Robert Cortright: 12, 15r, 20, 21, 24, 25, 27l, 27br, 28tr, 35r, 36, 37r, 57r, 65r, 80, 81r, 98;
Detroit Institute of Arts, Gift of P. L. Barter: 30;
Elizabeth Donoff: 29r;
Courtesy of George Eastman House: endpapers;
FBM Studio/Mancia/Bodmer: 70, 71r;
Figg Engineering Group: 94, 95r, 100, 101l, 101c;
Foto Marburg/Art Resource, New York: 56 (inset);
Giraudon/Art Resource, New York: 14, 20 (inset), 29l;
W. H. Guild, Jr./New York City Parks Photo Archive: 28br;
Hagley Museum and Library: 7, 44 (inset), 61t, 64, 65l, 103r; back cover (t);

Patrick Harbron: 82;
Historic American Engineering Record, Library of Congress: cover, 40, 42, 43l, 45 (inset), 48, 49br, 50, 51, 60, 61l, 61br;
Hong Kong Tourist Association: 110, 111l;
Honshu-Shikoku Bridge Authority: 2-3, 96, 97, 114, 115, 116, 117;
Hulton Getty/Tony Stone Images: 37l, 59, 74, 83r;
Nicholas Kane, Esto/Arcaid: 99r;
Darius Kinsey, from *Kinsey, Photographer*, courtesy David Bohn and Rodolfo Petschek: 66, 67;
Ronald G. Knapp: 18, 19;
Lake Havasu Tourism Bureau: 38 (inset);

Library of Congress: 49tr;
Joseph Ka-Kee Lee: 110 (inset), 111r;
Robert Loffredo: 22 (inset);
Richard Margolis: 5-6, 13c, 13cr, 41, 42 (inset), 63, 64 (inset);
Peter Mauss/Esto Photographics: 54/55;
W. Miles Wright/Frank H. McClung Museum, University of Tennessee, Knoxville: 101r;
Michigan Department of Transportation, Photography Unit: 88, 89, 125;
Municipal Archives, Department of Records and Information Services, City of New York: 1;
Museum of Modern Art, Film Stills Archive: 92l, 93;

National Archives: 86, 87;
National Monuments Record, Wales: 46 (inset);
John Nicols, University of Oregon: 14 (inset);
Oregon Department of Transportation: 80 (inset), 81l;
Providence Journal-Bulletin: 102 (inset);
Royal Commission on the Ancient and Historical Monuments of England: 62 (inset);
Rutgers University: 43r, 55tl, 55tr;
Engineering Collection in the Division of the History of Technology, Smithsonian Institution: 73br;
Springer/Corbis-Bettmann: 92r;
Storebaeltforbindelsen: 112, 113;

Strait Crossing, Inc.: 109l;
Brenda Tharp: 82 (inset);
Tourist Office of Spain: 99l;
Special Collections Division, University of Washington Libraries (Negative Numbers: Farquharson 4, 5, 6, 12): 84, 85;
Underwood Photo Archives, San Francisco: 15l, 16, 28l, 38, 54, 58, 79br, 83l, 83c;
UPI/Corbis-Bettmann: 55br, 73tr, 74 (inset), 75, 76, 79tr, 90, 91, 95l;
Courtesy of Welshpool Town Council, Montgomeryshire, Wales: 47r;
and Wolfgang Volz/Christo and Jeanne-Claude: 31r.